Trade up to a higher grade with CGP!

GCSE Business isn't easy, but you don't need to go it alone...
this fantastic CGP book is the perfect partner for your revision!

It's bursting with realistic exam-style questions on everything from
production to procurement — including the context-based questions
that are a big part of the Grade 9-1 exams.

We've also put answers to every question at the back of the book,
so once you've done the work, it's easy to ~~market~~ mark it.

CGP — still the best! ☺

Our sole aim here at CGP is to produce the highest quality books —
carefully written, immaculately presented and dangerously close to being funny.

Then we work our socks off to get them out to you
— at the cheapest possible prices.

How to Use This Book

- Hold the book <u>upright</u>, approximately <u>50 cm</u> from your face, ensuring that the text looks like <u>this</u>, not this. Alternatively, place the book on a <u>horizontal</u> surface (e.g. a table or desk) and sit adjacent to the book, at a distance which doesn't make the text too small to read.

- In case of emergency, press the two halves of the book together <u>firmly</u> in order to close.

- Before attempting to use this book, familiarise yourself with the following <u>safety information</u>:

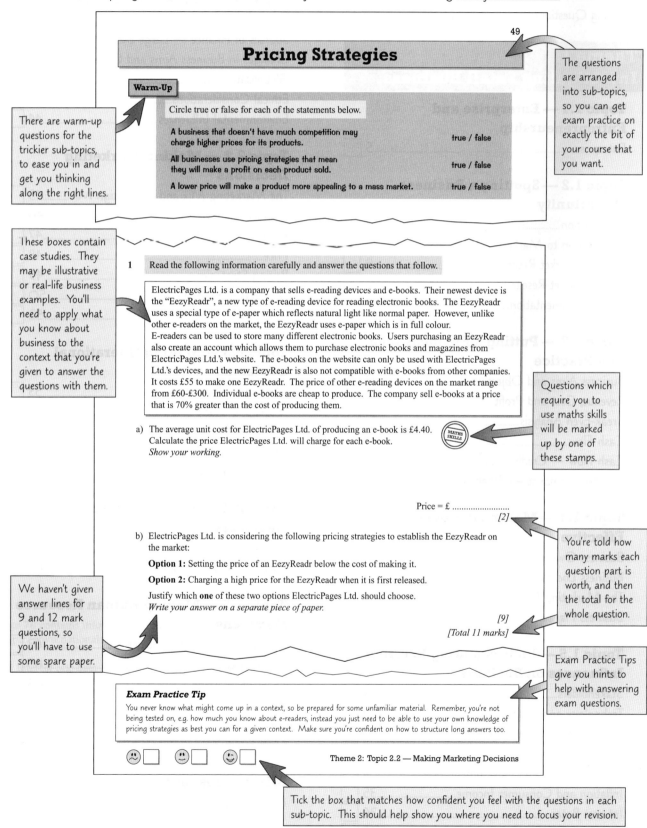

There are warm-up questions for the trickier sub-topics, to ease you in and get you thinking along the right lines.

The questions are arranged into sub-topics, so you can get exam practice on exactly the bit of your course that you want.

49

Pricing Strategies

Warm-Up

Circle true or false for each of the statements below.

A business that doesn't have much competition may charge higher prices for its products.　　true / false

All businesses use pricing strategies that mean they will make a profit on each product sold.　　true / false

A lower price will make a product more appealing to a mass market.　　true / false

These boxes contain case studies. They may be illustrative or real-life business examples. You'll need to apply what you know about business to the context that you're given to answer the questions with them.

1　Read the following information carefully and answer the questions that follow.

ElectricPages Ltd. is a company that sells e-reading devices and e-books. Their newest device is the "EezyReadr", a new type of e-reading device for reading electronic books. The EezyReadr uses a special type of e-paper which reflects natural light like normal paper. However, unlike other e-readers on the market, the EezyReadr uses e-paper which is in full colour.
E-readers can be used to store many different electronic books. Users purchasing an EezyReadr also create an account which allows them to purchase electronic books and magazines from ElectricPages Ltd.'s website. The e-books on the website can only be used with ElectricPages Ltd.'s devices, and the new EezyReadr is also not compatible with e-books from other companies. It costs £55 to make one EezyReadr. The price of other e-reading devices on the market range from £60-£300. Individual e-books are cheap to produce. The company sell e-books at a price that is 70% greater than the cost of producing them.

a) The average unit cost for ElectricPages Ltd. of producing an e-book is £4.40. Calculate the price ElectricPages Ltd. will charge for each e-book. *Show your working.*

Questions which require you to use maths skills will be marked up by one of these stamps.

Price = £ ....
[2]

b) ElectricPages Ltd. is considering the following pricing strategies to establish the EezyReadr on the market:

Option 1: Setting the price of an EezyReadr below the cost of making it.

Option 2: Charging a high price for the EezyReadr when it is first released.

Justify which **one** of these two options ElectricPages Ltd. should choose. *Write your answer on a separate piece of paper.*

[9]
[Total 11 marks]

You're told how many marks each question part is worth, and then the total for the whole question.

We haven't given answer lines for 9 and 12 mark questions, so you'll have to use some spare paper.

Exam Practice Tips give you hints to help with answering exam questions.

Exam Practice Tip

You never know what might come up in a context, so be prepared for some unfamiliar material. Remember, you're not being tested on, e.g. how much you know about e-readers, instead you just need to be able to use your own knowledge of pricing strategies as best you can for a given context. Make sure you're confident on how to structure long answers too.

Theme 2: Topic 2.2 — Making Marketing Decisions

Tick the box that matches how confident you feel with the questions in each sub-topic. This should help show you where you need to focus your revision.

The Exams

These two pages have some information and tips on what to expect in the exams, to help you do really well. You might find it useful to read through them before answering any questions, then you can put what you've read into practice.

There Are Two Exam Papers — Paper 1 and Paper 2

Paper 1

- Paper 1 is 1 hour and 30 minutes long.
- It's worth 90 marks and is 50% of your total Business GCSE.
- It'll test you on information from Theme 1 — Topics 1.1 to 1.5 of this book.

Paper 2

- Paper 2 is 1 hour and 30 minutes long.
- It's worth 90 marks and is 50% of your total Business GCSE.
- It'll test you on information from Theme 2 — Topics 2.1 to 2.5 of this book.

1) In both papers there'll be three sections.
2) Section A is a mixture of multiple choice, short and long questions. It's worth 35 marks.
3) Sections B and C are both based around a case study, which could include some data. You'll have to answer a mixture of short and long questions related to the information in each case study. Section B is worth 30 marks and Section C is worth 25 marks.

> There are lots of questions that are based on case studies throughout this book. These case studies may be illustrative examples, or real-life businesses. Don't worry that you don't know the details of each case study — the trick is to apply what you know about business in general to each situation.

The Examiners are Looking for Three Types of Skills

There are basically three types of skill and knowledge that you need to show to get marks in the exams:

Demonstrate knowledge and understanding

- This skill is about recalling, selecting and communicating.
- You need to show that you've got a really good understanding of the facts, and that you can use appropriate business terms, e.g. sole trader, marketing mix, revenue.

Apply knowledge and understanding

- This skill is all about applying what you know to different situations.
- Make sure your answer is relevant to the situation that's been described.
- For example, an exam question might tell you about a sole trader who wants to buy a new piece of equipment, and ask you to suggest how they could raise the necessary finance. Here, you wouldn't want to suggest that the company issue more shares (since only a limited company can have shares and sole traders are unlimited).

Analyse and evaluate to demonstrate understanding, make judgements and draw conclusions

- This skill is all about using evidence to make judgements and reach conclusions.
- For example, if you recommend that a business raise money using a loan rather than an overdraft, you need to explain why, using what you know about finance.
- Your ideas need to be structured in a logical way so that your arguments make sense.
- Often, these questions won't have a right answer. The important thing is using evidence from the question to support the conclusion you've come to.

Exam Practice Tip
So there are two exams and each is 1 hour and 30 minutes long. Remember the different skills the examiners will be looking for — knowing what they want can help you predict what to write for answers, and make your life a bit easier.

Answering Questions

Here's some information on the different types of questions you can get, and how you should answer each one.

Make Sure you Read the Question

1) Command words are just the bit of the question that tell you what to do.

2) You'll find answering exam questions much easier if you understand exactly what they mean:

Command word	What to do
State or Give	These words ask for a statement — you don't need to back it up with evidence.
Define	You need to write down what a term means.
Identify	You need to interpret data shown on a graph or in a table to get your answer.
Calculate	Some questions ask for a bit of maths. Remember to show your working.
Complete	You need to fill in the missing parts of some information you've been given (e.g. complete a table).
Outline	You need to make two main points about a business issue and link them together.
Explain	This means you need to give reasons for things. You need to show that you understand how business issues can impact other areas of a business.
Discuss	You should give a long answer, which describes and explains a business issue.
Analyse	This means "Examine in detail." You should talk about the main features of the thing you're analysing. Then explain how these features collectively affect the business.
Justify	You'll be given some information about a business and asked to recommend whether the business should do something, or to choose between two options for what the business could do.
Evaluate	You should discuss and analyse both sides of an issue. You should finish your answer with a conclusion giving an overall judgement.

3) In general, you'll need to spend more time and write more for questions that are worth more marks.

4) Questions with the command words discuss, analyse, justify or evaluate are worth the most — they'll be 6, 9 or 12 marks. For these questions, it might help to write a quick plan to make sure you don't miss anything, and to make sure you show all the skills from the previous page.

You'll have to Answer Questions About Case Studies

1) For questions that are based on case study information or on data, make sure you use evidence from the case study or data set as well as your knowledge of Business in your answer.

2) For questions using 'justify' or 'evaluate' command words, there will usually be advantages and disadvantages of a situation to think about — to get all the marks, you'll need to give both sides of the argument before coming to a conclusion.

You'll often have to consider how different parts of a business work together when answering case study questions.

3) Before you get started on your answer, read the case study and any data all the way through.

You'll be Tested on Your Maths Skills

1) In your exams, you'll have to do some maths — e.g. do some calculations using financial data, or interpret a graph.

2) For calculation questions, always make sure you show your working — even if your final answer's wrong, you could still get some marks if your method was correct.

In this book, questions that test your maths skills are shown by this stamp: **MATHS SKILLS**

3) And don't forget to take a calculator to the exams.

Exam Practice Tip

For each question in the exams, look at the command words and the number of marks. Remember that longer questions are usually testing your judgement as well as your knowledge, so you should support your ideas with evidence.

Enterprise

1   Which of the following is a purpose of business activity?
Put a cross (✗) in **one** correct box.

    A   To employ entrepreneurs.   ☐

    B   To provide goods.   ☐

    C   To be sustainable.   ☐

    D   To train employees.   ☐

[Total 1 mark]

2   Explain **one** reason why an entrepreneur might find setting up a business rewarding.

....

....

....

....

[Total 3 marks]

3   Explain **one** benefit of building a good brand image for a product.

....

....

....

....

[Total 3 marks]

4   Discuss the reasons why new business ideas may come about.

....

....

....

....

....

....

....

....

[Total 6 marks]

5 Discuss the responsibilities an entrepreneur needs to fulfil in order to run a new business.

....

....

....

....

....

....

....

....

....

[Total 6 marks]

6 Read the following information carefully and answer the questions that follow.

> Louise is starting a new company, Tasty Teas, which sells ready cooked meals.
> In order to start up Tasty Teas, Louise has taken out a loan from her bank.
> Unlike similar products on the market, the ingredients Louise uses to make the
> ready cooked meals are all ethically sourced and are very high quality. Louise
> also offers meal varieties that aren't available from other companies in the market.

a) Outline **one** risk to Louise of starting up Tasty Teas.

....

....

....

[2]

b) Outline **one** way that Louise has added value to ready cooked meals.

....

....

....

[2]

[Total 4 marks]

Exam Practice Tip

Businesses are started for all sorts of reasons. But whatever the business, the responsibilities of the entrepreneur who sets it up and runs it will be fairly similar. Make sure you know those responsibilities and can apply them in different situations.

Theme 1: Topic 1.1 — Enterprise and Entrepreneurship

Competition

1   Explain **one** reason why a business may decide to develop high quality products.

....

....

....

[Total 3 marks]

2   Read the following information carefully and answer the questions that follow.

> BlueBamboo, a company specialising in gadgets, spots a gap in the market for a new plant sensor. The company designs a sensor which detects the water and nutrient content of the soil in which it is placed and then transmits this information to a person's smartphone, to tell them when they need to water and feed their plants. The company decides to sell their new sensor under the name Shoot Sense at £110 per unit, and it first goes on sale in 2012.
>
> Three years after launching their sensor, BlueBamboo noticed that three other companies had launched similar products. The prices of the different plant sensors available in the market are shown in **Figure 1**. 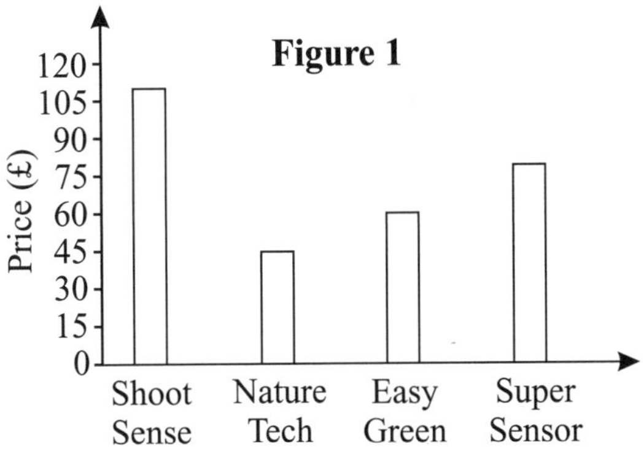
>
> **Figure 1** — Price (£) bar chart: Shoot Sense ≈ 110, Nature Tech ≈ 45, Easy Green ≈ 60, Super Sensor ≈ 80.
>
> BlueBamboo also noticed that its sales had stopped increasing, despite an increasing number of people choosing to buy plant sensors.
>
> The managers of BlueBamboo decided to carry out market research into customers' opinions. They found that many visitors to their website were confused with how to use Shoot Sense with their smartphone and were unable to get through to a customer services assistant when calling or emailing the company. Due to this confusion, many customers decided to buy a different brand of plant sensor. Customers who did buy Shoot Sense also stated that getting user training would be useful for getting the most out of its different features. Some customers who bought Shoot Sense online were unhappy with how long it took to arrive in the post.

a)   Outline **one** way in which Shoot Sense may have made BlueBamboo competitive in 2012.

....

....

[2]

b)   BlueBamboo are considering two options for increasing the sales of Shoot Sense:

   Option 1 — Reduce the price of Shoot Sense to £90.

   Option 2 — Invest in improvements to its customer service.

   Justify which **one** of these two options BlueBamboo should choose.
   Write your answer on a separate sheet of paper.

[9]

[Total 11 marks]

Introduction to Market Research

1 Which of the following explains what is meant by a gap in the market? Put a cross (✗) in **one** correct box.

A   A market in which there are very few competitors. ☐

B   A product that is unpopular with customers. ☐

C   A company that has failed. ☐

D   A customer need that isn't being met. ☐

[Total 1 mark]

2 Which of the following are types of customer needs? Put a cross (✗) in **two** correct boxes.

A   a reasonably priced product ☐

B   low unit costs ☐

C   convenience of where the product is sold ☐

D   the market share of a business ☐

E   the type of promotion used ☐

[Total 2 marks]

3 Read the following information carefully and answer the questions that follow.

> Davis and Sons is a business that sells suits. Davis and Sons decide to carry out market research into the demand for different suit colours in the market, in order to understand their customers' needs. They identify a gap in the market for a dark green suit not sold in other nearby shops.

a) State **one** customer need that Davis and Sons should consider, apart from different suit colours.

....

[1]

b) Outline how the market research that Davis and Sons are conducting may help them to reduce risks within the business

....

....

[2]

c) Outline **one** impact on Davis and Sons of identifying a gap in the market.

....

....

[2]

[Total 5 marks]

Theme 1: Topic 1.2 — Spotting a Business Opportunity

Types of Market Research

1 Which of the following is an example of secondary market research? Put a cross (✗) in **one** correct box.

A   focus groups   ☐

B   a survey   ☐

C   market reports   ☐

D   questionnaires   ☐

[Total 1 mark]

2 Explain **one** advantage to a small business of using secondary market research rather than primary market research.

....

....

....

[Total 3 marks]

3 Read the following information carefully and answer the questions that follow.

> A small publishing company called Best Publications is creating a new magazine for teenagers. It decides to carry out a number of focus groups throughout the process of making the magazine. They also carry out market research using social media.

a) Outline **one** factor that Best Publications should consider when carrying out the focus groups.

....

....

[2]

b) Outline how Best Publications may use social media in its market research.

....

....

[2]

> Before one of their early focus groups, the managers decide to leave a selection of magazines in the room where it is taking place. They then see which magazines the members of the focus group choose to browse through.

c) State what type of primary research Best Publications has used in this case.

....

[1]

[Total 5 marks]

Using Market Research

Circle qualitative or quantitative to show the type of data that best describes each of the following.

The percentage increase in profits for a business.   qualitative/quantitative

Customer opinions on the quality of service from a waiter.   qualitative/quantitative

Customer scores for products out of a maximum of five.   qualitative/quantitative

A graph showing the variation in sales of a product throughout a year.   qualitative/quantitative

1   Read the following information carefully and answer the question that follows.

Tom's Teas is a tea shop. Tom, the owner, has blended three new herbal teas to sell in his shop. He decides to carry out some market research to find out which of the teas is likely to be most successful.

Tom offers free samples of each tea in the shop and asks customers to fill in a short questionnaire about them. The questionnaire is shown in **Figure 1** on the right.

Figure 1

Q1	Which of the three herbal teas did you prefer?
	Jasmine deluxe ☐
	Camomile and nettle ☐
	Liquorice and mint ☐
	Didn't like any of them ☐
Q2	Was there any tea that you really disliked? Please explain your answer.
Q3	Would you buy one of these teas instead of another drink in the shop?

78% of the people who responded to the questionnaire preferred the jasmine deluxe tea, 10% preferred the camomile and nettle tea, 4% preferred the liquorice and mint tea and 8% didn't like any of them. A common answer to question 2 was that the liquorice and mint tea tasted bitter; however, there were few complaints about the other two teas. 52% of the people who responded to the questionnaire stated "No" for question 3.

Analyse the impact of this market research on the products that Tom's Teas offers.

....

....

....

....

....

....

....

....

....

....

[Total 6 marks]

2 Read the following information carefully and answer the questions that follow.

Georgina owns a restaurant called The RiverHouse Restaurant. The restaurant is in an old building, with oak beams and a large log fire. It is located on a country lane next to a river. She recently carried out a survey of some of her customers. She carried out the same survey five years previously. The results for one of the questions are shown in **Figure 2** below.

Figure 2

Q1 What is the most important aspect of a restaurant for you?

☐ the choice of food
☐ the atmosphere
■ the location
▨ the price

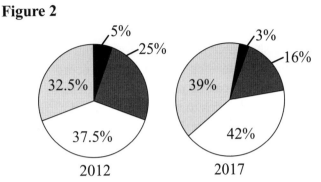

2012

2017

Before the survey, Georgina had flyers for her restaurant that showed a picture of the outside of the restaurant and displayed the price of her set menu. Afterwards, she changed her flyers to show an image of the inside, and a list of live music events that she is hosting.

a) Analyse the effect changing its flyers is likely to have on The RiverHouse Restaurant.

....

....

....

....

....

....

....

....

....

....

[6]

b) Georgina is considering two options for improving her business:

Option 1 — Improving the decorations and furniture inside the restaurant.

Option 2 — Increasing the number of choices on the menu.

Justify which **one** of these two options Georgina should choose.
Write your answer on a separate sheet of paper.

[9]

[Total 15 marks]

Exam Practice Tip

There's no easy way around these longer questions, you've just got to pay attention to all of the information you've been given. Then you can use it, as well as a bit of business knowledge, to recommend the most sensible option for a business.

 ☐   ☐   ☐

Theme 1: Topic 1.2 — Spotting a Business Opportunity

Market Segmentation

1 Read the following information carefully and answer the questions that follow.

MetroMusic is an established small business which sells CD players and other sound equipment. Playing vinyl records has become more fashionable in recent years, so the business has decided to start selling record players which can be used to play old vinyl records. It decides to sell a brand called The Groove. **Figure 1** on the right shows the market map for some brands of vinyl record players in the market based on price and quality. MetroMusic has used market segmentation to identify its target market.

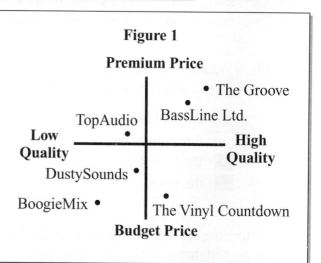

Figure 1

a) Complete the table below using the information in **Figure 1**.

Brand of record player	Price (£)	Quality
BassLine Ltd.	350	high
The Groove	580	high
1.	95	low
2.	130	moderate
TopAudio	200	moderate
The Vinyl Countdown	99	moderate

[1]

b) Define the term 'market segmentation'.

....

....

[1]

c) State **one** feature of MetroMusic's target market for its new record player.

....

[1]

d) Identify which of the other products on the market The Groove would be in competition with.

....

[1]

e) Outline **one** reason why a £150, relatively high quality record player may sell well.

....

....

[2]

[Total 6 marks]

Business Aims and Objectives

Warm-Up

Place the aims on the left into the correct column of the table, depending on whether they are financial or non-financial.

To have sales of £30 000

To have the challenge of running a business

To improve education in the community

To increase market share

Financial Aims	Non-financial Aims

1   Explain how business aims are different to business objectives.

....

....

....

[Total 3 marks]

2   Read the following information carefully and answer the questions that follow.

> Karen Booth is opening Karen's Sarnies, a small sandwich shop in Nantwich, Cheshire. Karen previously worked in a small café, but is opening a new business so she can have more control over the menu she serves and the ingredients she uses. In her first year, Karen's main aim is for the business to survive. For the years after that, Karen has other aims, such as to maximise profit.
> One of Karen's main competitors will be Rye Ltd., a café in the neighbouring street.
> Rye Ltd. has been open for ten years and is popular within the town.

a) State **one** non-financial aim that Karen Booth has for her business.

....

[1]

b) Outline **one** reason why the aims for Rye Ltd. are likely to be different to the aims for Karen's Sarnies.

....

....

....

....

[2]

[Total 3 marks]

3 | Read the following information carefully and answer the questions that follow.

> At the start of 2008, Ole opened Merino, a business selling Scandinavian knitwear in the UK. When he started the company, he set and stuck to the following aims:
>
> 1. To make knitted garments using pure wool, sourced from Scandinavia.
> 2. To have sales of over £120 000 per year by the eighth year.
>
> Ole also set the company yearly sales targets, increasing to £120 000 for the eighth year.
>
> For the first three years, Ole was selling his knitwear on the internet. Then, in 2011, a retailer with three outlets in his local area started stocking his products. In 2013, Ole put some adverts for his company in a national newspaper. This led to many more orders on his website, and in 2014 a national department store offered to start stocking his products. This offer would increase Ole's sales from the current level of £150 000 per year to a predicted £180 000 per year. However, in order to make products at a cost that the department store would be willing to pay, Ole would have to start using a cheaper, synthetic wool. Ole decided to decline the offer from the department store, and continue selling his products through other outlets.

a) Outline **one** reason Ole has set himself yearly sales targets.

....

....

....

[2]

b) Calculate the predicted percentage increase in sales that Merino would have had if Ole had accepted the deal with the national department store. *Show your working.*

.... %

[2]

c) Analyse the impact on Merino of Ole's sticking to his aims.

....

....

....

....

....

....

....

....

[6]

[Total 10 marks]

Theme 1: Topic 1.3 — Putting a Business Idea into Practice

Revenue, Cost and Profit

Circle the costs below that would be described as 'fixed costs' for a business.

raw materials   running machinery   insurance   wages for factory staff   managers' salaries

---

1   Which of the following is the correct definition of revenue?
Put a cross (✗) in **one** correct box.

A   The amount of money a company receives from sales.   ☐

B   The amount of money left over after costs are taken into account.   ☐

C   The amount of money paid out to shareholders.   ☐

D   The total amount of costs over a year.   ☐

[Total 1 mark]

---

2   Which of the following would be the interest on a loan of £26 000, which was repaid to a total of £27 720? Put a cross (✗) in **one** correct box.

A   10%   ☐

B   0.7%   ☐

C   6.2%   ☐

D   6.6%   ☐

[Total 1 mark]

---

3   A new business makes scarves and sells them for £7. **Figure 1** shows the number of scarves sold by the business in three years and the total costs for each year.

a) Complete **Figure 1** to show the total money received from sales for Years 2 and 3.

	Year 1	Year 2	Year 3
Number of scarves sold	850	450	1200
Total money received	5950	....	....
Total costs (£)	4700	3600	6200

Figure 1

[2]

b) Identify the year in which the business made a loss.

....

[1]

[Total 3 marks]

Theme 1: Topic 1.3 — Putting a Business Idea into Practice

Cash Flow — Credit

1 Yoo Too Sunglasses Ltd. gives its customers 2 months credit to pay.
Figure 1 shows an incomplete cash flow statement for Yoo Too Sunglasses Ltd.

£	Apr	May	Jun	Jul	Aug	Sep	Oct
Cash Flow Statement — Yoo Too Sunglasses Ltd.							
Total orders this month (for payment in 2 months)	1000	1300	1400	1500	1300	400	300
Cash inflow	300	350	1000	1300	....	1500	1300
Cash outflow	1000	1200	1300	....	1250	300	200
Net cash flow	(700)	....	(300)	(50)	150	1200	1100
Opening balance	1300	600	....	(550)	(600)	(450)	750
Closing balance	600	(250)	(550)	(600)	(450)	750	....

Figure 1

a) Define the term 'opening balance'.

....

[1]

b) Define the term 'closing balance'.

....

[1]

c) Complete **Figure 1** by filling in the blanks, assuming that all customers make their payment 2 months after their order has been placed. Use the space below for your working.

[5]

d) There is an unexpected rise in demand for sunglasses in November.
Analyse the impact this may have on Yoo Too Sunglasses Ltd.'s cash flow.

....

....

....

....

....

....

....

....

[6]

[Total 13 marks]

Theme 1: Topic 1.3 — Putting a Business Idea into Practice

Sources of Finance — Small Businesses

1   Which of the following describes a short term source
of finance? Put a cross (✗) in **one** correct box.

A   overdraft   ☐

B   retained profit   ☐

C   share capital   ☐

D   bank loan   ☐

[Total 1 mark]

2   Explain **one** disadvantage to a business of using trade credit.

....

....

....

[Total 3 marks]

3   Explain **one** reason why a venture capitalist may help to fund a new, risky business.

....

....

....

[Total 3 marks]

4   Read the following information carefully and answer the questions that follow.

In 2016, Nadia decided to become a freelance photographer. She used a crowd funding website
and a loan from her bank in order to set up her photography business. In the first year of her
business her costs were high but she did not have many bookings. She has decided to obtain
a new source of finance in order to promote her business more widely in her second year.

a) Define the term 'crowd funding'.

....

....

[1]

b) Outline **one** reason why Nadia may not be able to use retained profits in order to finance the costs
in the second year of her business.

....

....

[2]

[Total 3 marks]

Business Ownership Structures

Draw circles to show whether the statements below are **true** or **false**.

1) Private limited companies can only sell new shares if all current shareholders agree.   TRUE / FALSE

2) Partners generally have an equal share in a company.   TRUE / FALSE

3) A franchisor will usually get all the profits made by a franchisee.   TRUE / FALSE

4) Sole trader businesses have shares that can be bought and sold by anybody.   TRUE / FALSE

1   Which of the following is an advantage of being a sole trader? Put a cross (✗) in **one** correct box.

A   A sole trader has a partner to take care of running the business. ☐

B   It's easy and relatively cheap to start up as a sole trader. ☐

C   A sole trader can't lose more money than they've invested in the business. ☐

D   It's easy for the business to grow by making shares available for anyone to buy. ☐

[Total 1 mark]

2   Explain **one** disadvantage of a sole trader business structure.

....

....

....

....

[Total 3 marks]

3   Explain **one** benefit to shareholders if a business has limited liability.

....

....

....

....

[Total 3 marks]

4 Explain how a partnership works.

....

....

....

....

[Total 3 marks]

5 Read the following information carefully and answer the questions that follow.

Blackwell's Pies is a partnership that was started 15 years ago by Keith Blackwell and his wife Moira. The company makes pies that are stocked by small businesses, such as farm shops. Recently, Blackwell's Pies has been given a contract to supply pies to a leading supermarket chain, which means the business will need to finance a large expansion project. Keith Blackwell is going to make the company a private limited company, and sell some shares in the company to his son and brother-in-law.

The percentage ownership of the company when it is a partnership and a private limited company are shown in **Figure 1** below.

Figure 1

Name	Percentage owned of partnership	Percentage owned of private limited company
Keith Blackwell	50%	
Moira Blackwell	50%	30%
Anthony Blackwell	0%	25%
Graham Williams	0%	15%

a) Identify the percentage of the company that Keith Blackwell will own once it is a private limited company.

....

[1]

b) Analyse the impact that becoming a private limited company will have on Blackwell's Pies.

....

....

....

....

....

....

....

[6]

[Total 7 marks]

6 Read the following information carefully and answer the question that follows.

> Kate has just qualified as an accountant and wants to open an accountancy firm. Although she has managed to get a bank loan, she doesn't have a lot of money to put into the business. Somebody she studied with has suggested that they start the business together, as a partnership. Kate doesn't know this person well, and is unsure whether they share her vision for the business.

Kate is considering whether to start her business as a partnership with her acquaintance. Justify whether or not Kate should start up her business as a partnership.
Write your answer on a separate piece of paper.

[Total 9 marks]

7 Read the following information carefully and answer the questions that follow.

> Isaac works in marketing, but also runs a dog sitting business in his spare time. He is planning to leave his marketing job so that he can focus on his dog sitting business. Isaac has a lot of experience in caring for dogs, but is wary of looking after other types of animals, as he doesn't have much knowledge about caring for them.
>
> Isaac is planning to set up a franchise of Petpals™, an established, well-regarded company that operates throughout the UK. Franchisees of *Petpals* are able to offer the following services: pet sitting (for cats and other small animals), dog walking, home boarding, puppy care, elderly dog care, pet taxi services, microchips and medication.
>
> The typical investment needed to become a *Petpals* franchisee is around £20 000 in the first year. This covers an initial payment to *Petpals* of £12 500, as well as costs needed to set up the business, such as a van that is safe for pets to travel in. As a franchisee of *Petpals*, Isaac will be offered guidance and training, including assistance writing a business plan and setting up a marketing campaign before the franchise is launched. *Petpals* will also give Isaac training before the franchise is launched.

a) Define the term 'franchise'.

....

....

[1]

b) Evaluate whether setting up as a franchise of *Petpals* will benefit Isaac.
You should use the information provided, as well as your knowledge of business.
Write your answer on a separate piece of paper.

[12]

[Total 13 marks]

Exam Practice Tip
The devil's in the detail where business ownership structures are concerned. Make sure you know the differences between sole traders, partnerships, private limited companies and franchises, along with the advantages and disadvantages of each.

Theme 1: Topic 1.4 — Making the Business Effective

Business Location

1   Which of the following businesses is most likely to prioritise the location of
    the market when choosing where to locate? Put a cross (✗) in **one** correct box.

    A   A company that sells stationery over the internet.   ☐

    B   A hairdresser.   ☐

    C   A courier service that delivers items nationally.   ☐

    D   A company that arranges package holidays over the phone.   ☐

    [Total 1 mark]

2   Explain **one** disadvantage to a business of locating near businesses of the same type.

    ....

    ....

    ....

    ....

    [Total 3 marks]

3   Read the following information carefully and answer the questions that follow.

    > DP Oak Ltd. are a new company that make flat-pack wardrobes which
    > they sell over the internet. They are deciding where to locate their factory.

    a) Outline why locating close to the market may not be a priority for DP Oak Ltd.

    ....

    ....

    ....

    [2]

    b) DP Oak Ltd. are considering two possible sites for the factory:

    •   **Option 1:** site 1 — a site on an industrial estate 10 miles from the town of Hampton, an area
        of high unemployment. The industrial estate is on a local bus route and near a college.
        It is 35 miles away from the nearest wood processing plant.

    •   **Option 2:** site 2 — a site on the outskirts of Tawbridge, a town with high levels of
        employment that is 30 miles away from Hampton. The site is 2 miles from the nearest
        wood processing plant, and has a number of other, similar businesses operating nearby.

    Justify which **one** of the two options DP Oak Ltd. should choose.
    Write your answer on a separate piece of paper.

    [9]

    [Total 11 marks]

Exam Practice Tip

The best location for a company largely depends on the type of business it is. If you get asked about the location of a
particular business in the exam, think about things such as what it sells, who (and where) it sells to, the amount and type
of labour it's likely to need, and the relative transport costs into and out of the site.

The Marketing Mix

Fill in the gaps in the following passage using the correct words from the list on the right.

The different elements of the marketing mix include product, price, promotion and .... The product being sold should be something that customers .... and the price must be .... Promoting a product includes .... it.

want   have

place

cheap

good value

population

advertising

analysing

1   Read the following information carefully and answer the questions that follow.

> Ananda owns a sportswear company, WorkOut Ltd. He spends a large amount of money regularly researching customer preferences in sportswear and ensuring that customers who own his products enjoy them and find them attractive. His products are relatively expensive. His brand is not very well known except amongst fitness experts. He sells his products through retailers in gyms. He is also considering using e-commerce to sell his products.

a) Define the term 'e-commerce'.

....

[1]

b) Outline **one** aspect of the marketing mix that has been prioritised by Ananda.

....

....

[2]

c) Outline **one** advantage to Ananda of regularly assessing customer needs.

....

....

[2]

[Total 5 marks]

2   Explain **one** reason why a small business may sell products at higher prices than larger businesses.

....

....

....

[Total 3 marks]

3   Explain **one** way in which the product range of a smaller business may differ to that of a larger business.

....

....

....

[Total 3 marks]

4   Read the following information carefully and answer the questions that follow.

> Williamson's is an established kitchenware store in a shopping centre. It sells high quality kitchen goods, including pots, pans, cutlery, crockery and items used for baking. Each product is sold with a 15% profit margin. Most of the customers who visit the store come because they have heard about it from friends.
> Recently, a competitor kitchenware store, DiscountDishes, opened in the same shopping centre as Williamson's. DiscountDishes sells similar items to Williamson's but at a lower price, and slightly lower quality. It doesn't sell certain specialty items that Williamson's sells. DiscountDishes has posters up at the entrance to the shopping centre and is offering a free spatula to any customer who spends over £15 in store.

a) Outline how Williamson's products contribute to it having a successful marketing mix.

....

....

[2]

b) Analyse the impact that the opening of Discount Dishes may have on Williamson's marketing mix.

....

....

....

....

....

....

....

....

[6]

[Total 8 marks]

Exam Practice Tip

The way that small businesses balance the elements of their marketing mix can vary a lot from business to business.
If you get a question on a business's marketing mix make sure you've read the information given really carefully, and try to pick out the 4 Ps of the marketing mix for that business so you can then apply it to the question.

Business Plans

1   Which of the following pieces of information would you expect to find in a business plan? Put a cross (✗) in **two** correct boxes.

     A   Laws the business will have to follow.   ☐

     B   How the business will communicate with its employees.   ☐

     C   Where the business will be located.   ☐

     D   Forecasts of bar gate stock graphs.   ☐

     E   What the business idea is.   ☐

[Total 2 marks]

2   Read the following information carefully and answer the questions that follow.

> Sam wants to start a business manufacturing and selling flavoured marshmallows. Before starting up the business, Sam writes a business plan.
>
> Sam identifies a target market for the business, and a suitable price for his marshmallows. This allows him to set a budget for setting up the business in his plan. His plan also includes financial forecasts of revenue, material costs, profit and cash flow for the first five years.

a) State how Sam could have identified the target market for his business.

....

[1]

b) Outline **one** further piece of financial information that Sam should include in his plan.

....

....

[2]

[Total 3 marks]

3   Discuss the benefits to a business of writing a business plan.

....

....

....

....

....

....

....

[Total 6 marks]

Stakeholders

1 Read the following information carefully and answer the questions that follow.

> Heyshore Sports Ltd. are a company that own a sports centre in the town of Heyshore. In the last five years, their revenue has increased by 36% and profits have increased by 20%. As a result of this success, they have increased staff wages by 5% and cut the membership fees they charge their customers by 3%. They have also invested in refurbishing their changing rooms and have started investing in new gym equipment designed for children.
>
> Heyshore Sports Ltd. would like to expand their business by building more outdoor facilities. They are considering using an area of meadowland directly behind the sports centre. The land is currently a popular picnic spot for families, although a local environmental group tries to dissuade people from using the land as it's home to lots of wild plant and animal species. Another option is to use land 500 metres down the road from the sports centre. The land is currently occupied by a derelict factory, which would need knocking down and removing before any building could begin. This site is twice the size of the meadowland and the building work is expected to be more expensive.

a) Outline **one** way in which Heyshore Sports Ltd. may have satisfied the objectives of their customers.

....

....

[2]

b) Outline **one** reason why the government may have been satisfied with Heyshore Sports Ltd.'s business activities.

....

....

[2]

c) Outline **one** reason why some of Heyshore Sports Ltd.'s owners may have disagreed with the decision to increase staff wages by 5%.

....

....

[2]

d) Heyshore Sports Ltd. want to avoid too much conflict from stakeholders when they decide on a site for their expansion. They need to choose between:

Option 1: The area of meadowland behind the sports centre.

Option 2: The disused factory site 500 metres down the road from the sports centre.

Justify which **one** of these two options Heyshore Sports Ltd. should choose.

Write your answer on a separate piece of paper.

[9]

[Total 15 marks]

Technology and Business

1 Which **two** of the following are disadvantages of keeping up to date with technology in business? Put a cross (✗) in **two** correct boxes.

A   It can be very expensive. ☐

B   It usually makes processes slower. ☐

C   It limits the ways that businesses can communicate with customers. ☐

D   It can often mean that staff have to be retrained. ☐

E   It often limits the ways that businesses can promote their products. ☐

[Total 2 marks]

2   Read the following information carefully and answer the questions that follow.

Luanne owns a business that sells personalised children's gifts. Since starting the business at the start of 2016, her sales have continued to increase, as shown in **Figure 1**. She started her business by selling her products on a market stall but had an e-commerce website developed as well. She has been thinking about accepting PayPal as a form of payment on her website. Luanne would have to a pay a fee for using PayPal, but it would allow customers to pay for their items by entering their PayPal user name and password, rather than the details of their credit or debit card.

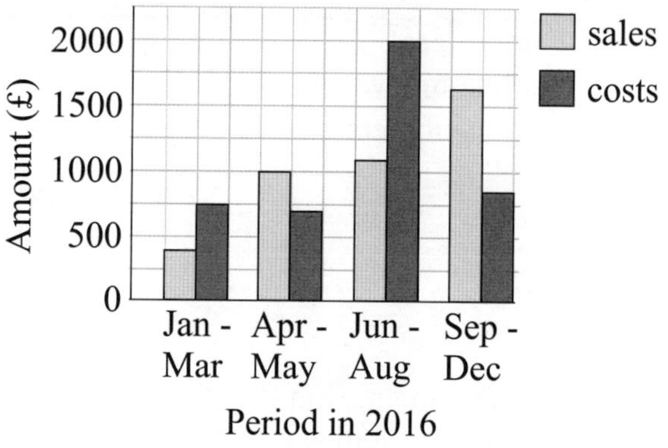

Figure 1

a)   Identify the 3-month period in which Luanne set up her website.

....

[1]

b)   Outline **one** benefit to Luanne of setting up her website.

....

....

[2]

c)   Outline **one** advantage to Luanne of accepting PayPal as a form of payment on her website.

....

....

....

[2]

[Total 5 marks]

3 Read the following information carefully and answer the questions that follow.

Special Pets and More is a pet shop located in a city suburb. As well as selling pet supplies, the business has also started selling small animals that need new homes. The first ten animals it had sold very quickly and customers buying them also tended to buy cages, food and accessories from the shop. Following this success, the owners rented the building next door to the shop to accommodate more animals and employed two new staff members to help to care for them.

The business advertises the animals it has for re-homing by placing adverts in its shop windows but currently the business is struggling to sell the animals it has. The owners are considering having a mobile app developed which would allow users to see statistics, pictures and video clips of the animals it has for re-homing and how much they cost.

a) State **one** digital method, other than mobile apps, that Special Pets and More could use to communicate with its customers.

....
[1]

b) Outline **one** way that the development of the mobile app would change Special Pets and More's marketing mix.

....

....

....
[2]

c) Analyse the impact that having a mobile app developed could have on Special Pets and More.

....

....

....

....

....

....

....

....
[6]

[Total 9 marks]

Exam Practice Tip
When you're given information about a business in the exam, make sure you read it all really carefully and use it to answer the questions. The examiners will want to see that you can apply your business knowledge to the specific situation they've given you — if you just randomly rattle off as much as you know about a topic you'll miss out on marks.

   Theme 1: Topic 1.5 — Understanding External Influences on Business

Employment and the Law

Tick the three situations below that are breaking employment law.

An accountancy firm only recruits people who are under 50 years old. ☐

A nursery pays female supervisors more than male supervisors. ☐

750 grams of hamster food is sold in packaging that states it contains 1 kg. ☐

A jewellery maker sells necklaces with clasps that break easily. ☐

A sports centre refuses to recruit anyone who needs to use a wheelchair. ☐

1 Under the Health and Safety at Work Act, businesses have to take responsibility for the health and safety of their employees while they are at work. Coffee Tonight is a coffee chain that strictly follows this law, whereas Au Lait is a coffee chain that doesn't always follow this law.

a) State **two** possible consequences for Au Lait of not following this law.

....

....
[2]

b) Outline **one** disadvantage to Coffee Tonight of following this law.

....

....
[2]

[Total 4 marks]

2 Entertainment World is a UK company that runs a series of theme parks.
By law, Entertainment World must pay its staff at least the national minimum wage.

a) Outline **one** advantage to Entertainment World of paying its staff the minimum wage.

....

....
[2]

b) Outline **one** disadvantage to Entertainment World of paying its staff the minimum wage.

....

....
[2]

[Total 4 marks]

Consumer Law

1 Read the following information carefully and answer the questions that follow.

> Bill has started up a business selling used DVDs, called Bill's Films. He buys 50 used DVDs and checks each one for faults. He goes through the following checklist for each DVD:
>
> 1   Does the DVD play from beginning to end without stopping?   pass/fail
> 2   Does the DVD case match the DVD inside?   pass/fail
>
> If a DVD fails either of the tests above then he still sells it as it is, without labelling any defects, but at a discount price. He sells the remaining DVDs at a higher price.

a) State **one** reason why Bill's Films is breaking consumer law.

....
[1]

b) State **one** thing that Bill's customers are legally entitled to if a DVD they purchase does not meet legal requirements.

....
[1]

c) State **one** change that Bill can make to his business in order to keep to the requirements of consumer law.

....
[1]

[Total 3 marks]

2 Explain **one** way in which the profit of a business might be affected if its products don't meet legal requirements.

....

....

....

....
[Total 3 marks]

3 Explain **one** way in which a business might respond if there is a change in consumer law.

....

....

....

....
[Total 3 marks]

34

Unemployment and Government Taxes

1 Explain **one** way in which high unemployment may cause problems for a business.

....

....

....

[Total 3 marks]

2 Explain **one** advantage to a business of starting up while unemployment levels are high.

....

....

....

[Total 3 marks]

3 Read the following information carefully and answer the questions that follow.

> Country Rides is a small horse riding business. It has built up popularity since it opened five years ago, and now many of its horse riding trips become fully booked weeks in advance. The business faces very little competition and the owners think the business could be more profitable if they invested in more land and more horses. Before deciding whether to invest they are considering some of the predicted changes in taxation in the coming years. It is predicted that income tax is set to fall and the tax small businesses have to pay is set to rise.

a) Outline **one** advantage to Country Rides of a fall in income tax.

....

....

[2]

b) Analyse the impact on Country Rides of a rise in the tax that small businesses have to pay.

....

....

....

....

....

....

....

....

[6]

[Total 8 marks]

Theme 1: Topic 1.5 — Understanding External Influences on Business

Inflation and Consumer Income

1   Explain **one** reason why a UK business which sells products globally may benefit when the inflation rate in the UK is low.

....

....

....

[Total 3 marks]

2   **Figure 1** shows the percentage change in inflation and the average weekly wages in **country A** every year between 2006 and 2017.

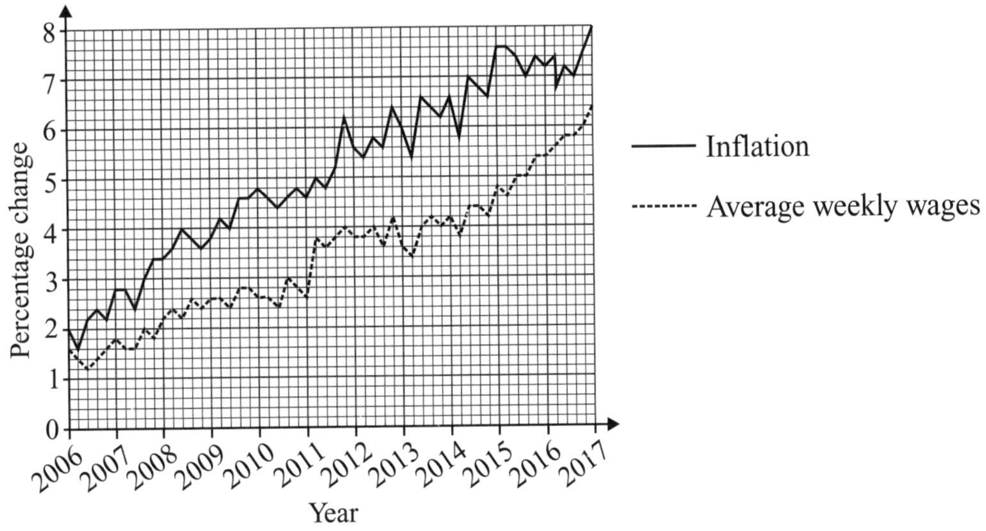

Figure 1

a) Identify the year between 2006 and 2017 during which inflation first reached a percentage change of 5%.

....

[1]

b) Identify the percentage change in average weekly wages at the start of 2015.

....

[1]

c) Explain how the difference in the rate of increase of inflation and average weekly wages may have affected businesses which sell luxury items in **country A**, between 2006 and 2017.

....

....

....

....

[3]

[Total 5 marks]

     Theme 1: Topic 1.5 — Understanding External Influences on Business

Interest Rates

1   Which of the following groups will benefit most from high interest rates? Put a cross (✗) in **one** correct box.

     A   People with mortgages on their houses.   ☐

     B   Banks that lend money to businesses.   ☐

     C   Small businesses that have borrowed money.   ☐

     D   Consumers who want to buy products.   ☐

[Total 1 mark]

2   **Figure 1** shows how interest rates changed in a country between 1900 and 2010.

a)   Identify which year was the most expensive for borrowing money.

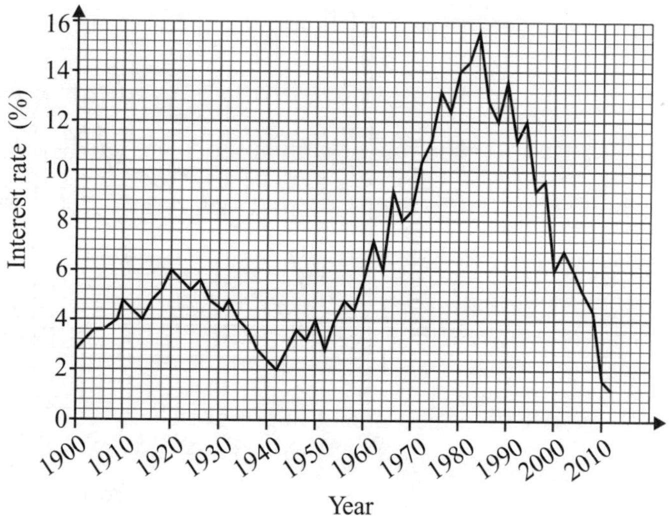

....
[1]

b)   State a reason for your answer to a).

....

....
[1]

Figure 1

c)   Explain how the overall trend in interest rates between 1980 and 2010 may have affected consumer spending.

....

....

....

....

....

[3]

[Total 5 marks]

Exam Practice Tip

This isn't the easiest topic to get your head around, so take your time when answering these questions.
For questions about the impact of changing interest rates on spending, think about what kind of effect a high or low interest rate would have on the cost of <u>borrowing</u>. How much people can borrow will affect what they <u>spend</u>.

Theme 1: Topic 1.5 — Understanding External Influences on Business

Exchange Rates

Warm-Up

Fill in the gaps in the following passage, using the words on the right.

.... are goods that are bought from a different country.

.... are goods that are sold to a different country.

If the value of the British pound decreases, British exports will be

.... abroad.

more expensive

imports

exports

cheaper

1   Which of the following statements best describes what is
    meant by an 'exchange rate'? Put a cross (✗) in **one** correct box.

   A   The price at which products are sold.   ☐

   B   The rate at which goods are exchanged between countries.   ☐

   C   The rate at which one country imports products from another.   ☐

   D   The price at which one currency can be traded for another.   ☐

   [Total 1 mark]

2   A Chinese company that makes hats buys some of its raw materials from India.
    The company sells its products worldwide. Most of its income comes from the USA.

a) The value of India's currency (INR) falls against China's currency (CNY).
    Explain how this change in exchange rate may affect how much it costs the
    Chinese company to make their hats.

   ....

   ....

   ....

   ....

   [3]

b) The value of the USA's currency (USD) rises against China's currency (CNY).
    Explain how this change in exchange rate may affect the sales of the hats.

   ....

   ....

   ....

   ....

   [3]

   [Total 6 marks]

   Theme 1: Topic 1.5 — Understanding External Influences on Business

Business Growth

Warm-Up

Draw lines to match the following methods of growth with their correct description.

Method	Description
merger	When a firm grows by buying more than half the shares in another firm.
	When two firms join together to form a new, but larger firm.
takeover	When a firm grows by expanding its own activities.

1   Explain **one** disadvantage of expanding by internal growth.

....

....

....

[Total 3 marks]

2   Purrfect Catz Ltd. make cat accessories. They are planning to grow their business by setting up a website to sell their products through. Outline **one** benefit of growing in this way.

....

....

....

[Total 2 marks]

3   Discuss how a business might expand by organic growth.

....

....

....

....

....

....

....

[Total 6 marks]

4   Read the following information carefully and answer the questions that follow.

> Relish the Day are a company that make jams and chutneys. They have recently taken over Bailes Farming Ltd., a company that had been supplying them with fruit and vegetables. Before the takeover, Bailes Farming Ltd. was struggling financially and was on the brink of closing. Relish the Day restructured the hierarchy of Bailes Farming Ltd. This involved making some staff redundant and also moving some employees from Relish the Day into management positions at Bailes Farming Ltd.

a) Outline **one** reason why Relish the Day may have chosen to take over Bailes Farming Ltd.

....

....

[2]

b) **Figure 1** below shows the average number of jars produced and the average costs per week for Relish the Day before and after the expansion. Complete **Figure 1** with the **one** missing figure.

MATHS SKILLS

	Before expansion	After expansion
Average number of jars made per week	120 000	200 000
Average costs per week	£151 200	£224 000
Average cost per jar	£1.26	

Figure 1

[1]

c) Outline **one** reason why the expansion may have led to lower average unit costs for Relish the Day.

....

....

....

[2]

d) Analyse the likely impact of restructuring the hierarchy of Bailes Farm Ltd. on Relish the Day.

....

....

....

....

....

....

....

....

....

[6]

[Total 11 marks]

Globalisation

1   Explain **one** way businesses face barriers to international trade.

....

....

....

....

[Total 3 marks]

2   Read the following information carefully and answer the questions that follow.

> Squishie is a multinational that makes smoothies and fruit juice. Their factory is in
> the UK, but they grow most of their fruit in Spain and sell their products to a global
> market. Squishee is considering setting up a factory in Spain. The company employs
> factory workers in the UK and farm workers in Spain who are each paid the minimum
> wage of their country. In one year, the business paid its workers the minimum wage
> of €756.7 per month in Spain, and €1378.9 per month in the UK.

a) Define the term 'multinational'.

....

[1]

b) Outline **one** benefit to Squishie of setting up a factory in Spain.

....

....

....

[2]

[Total 3 marks]

3   Discuss how a business may change its marketing mix in order to compete internationally.

....

....

....

....

....

....

....

....

[Total 6 marks]

Ethical Considerations

1 Which **two** of the following actions might a business take to improve its ethics? Put a cross (✗) in **two** correct boxes.

    A   Making sure factory workers work at least 10 hours per day. ☐

    B   Criticising competitor products in advertising material. ☐

    C   Setting up codes of conduct for factories. ☐

    D   Buying the cheapest raw materials possible from farmers in developing countries. ☐

    E   Paying staff in low-income countries above the minimum wage. ☐

[Total 2 marks]

2 Pharmacuticles is a firm which specialises in hair and nail beauty products. Like many companies, Pharmacuticles has its own ethical policies.

a) State **one** ethical consideration that Pharmacuticles may have for its employees.

....

[1]

b) State **one** ethical consideration that Pharmacuticles may have in product development.

....

[1]

[Total 2 marks]

3 Read the following information carefully and answer the question that follows.

> Beancraft Ltd. is a UK company that makes coffee. It buys coffee beans from plantations in less economically developed countries. Unlike most of its competitors in the UK, Beancraft Ltd. only uses plantations that have been certified by a fair trade organisation. There are more plantations worldwide that are not Fair Trade certified than those that are.

Analyse the impact of using a source of coffee beans that is Fair Trade certified on Beancraft Ltd.

....

....

....

....

....

....

....

....

....

[Total 6 marks]

Theme 2: Topic 2.1 — Growing the Business

Environmental Influences

1 Explain **one** disadvantage of a business being targeted
by a pressure group to improve its environmental policies.

....

....

....

....

[Total 3 marks]

2 Read the following information carefully and answer the questions that follow.

ForKids, a company which makes plastic children's toys, has just opened a new factory near a residential area. The factory has several pieces of machinery for making toys. Recently ForKids has received a complaint from a nearby resident about the noise from the factory.

Once the toys have been made, they are packaged individually in large cardboard boxes and transported in vans to distribution centres throughout the country.

a) Outline **one** way in which the managers of ForKids could minimise the impact of the new factory on the surrounding environment.

....

....

[2]

b) Outline **one** advantage to ForKids of making the new factory more environmentally friendly.

....

....

[2]

c) Outline **one** disadvantage to ForKids of making the new factory more environmentally friendly.

....

....

[2]

[Total 6 marks]

Exam Practice Tip

Whenever you get a context like the one in question 2 here, make sure you use as much of the information you're given as possible. The context will probably have lots of little hints for you to pick up on. Then it's your job to interpret the information and apply it to the question you're given. It's not always easy, but at least you have plenty of practice here.

The Marketing Mix and the Design Mix

Warm-Up

Circle the different elements below that make up the design mix of a product.

the place where
the product is sold

the aesthetics of
the product

the cost of making
the product

how functional
the product is

the price that the
product will be sold for

1 Which of the following describes what is meant by product differentiation? Put a cross (✗) in **one** correct box.

A   making lots of different products ☐

B   making a product distinctive in the market ☐

C   when a product is more successful than competitors' products ☐

D   when the sales of a product change over its life cycle ☐

[Total 1 mark]

2 Read the following information carefully and answer the questions that follow.

> SwimTech is a company that sells sportswear gadgets, particularly for swimmers.
> The business's newest product is a waterproof watch which can track a swimmer's progress.
> Unlike similar products on the market, the watch can be used alongside other gadgets such
> as underwater headphones and MP3 players, to allow the swimmer to pick music.
> SwimTech decides to sell the product mainly through high street retailers.

a) Outline **one** way in which SwimTech's choice of method of distribution may affect the way its new product is promoted.

....

....

[2]

b) Outline **one** benefit to SwimTech of making its watch different to other products on the market.

....

....

[2]

[Total 4 marks]

Exam Practice Tip

There are lots of ways in which changing one element of the marketing mix can affect other elements, e.g. increasing the price of a product may affect how it is promoted. You could get asked about any combination of the different elements of the marketing mix, so make sure you're confident at explaining the impact of one element on another.

 ☐   ☐   ☐

Price

1   Explain **one** impact of operating in a competitive market on the pricing strategy of a business.

....

....

....

....

[Total 3 marks]

2   Explain **one** reason why using technology can allow a business to lower its prices.

....

....

....

....

[Total 3 marks]

3   Read the following information carefully and answer the questions that follow.

> Jerome runs Pottery Wheel, a pottery company. His team make four different collections
> of products. Their first collection "Indigo Night" has been declining in popularity.
> Their newest collection "Crystal Gold" is of better quality than their other collections.
> It is being targeted at a more luxurious market than the other collections.

a)   Outline why Jerome may choose to lower the pricing of "Indigo Night" in the future.

....

....

....

[2]

b)   Outline why the Crystal Gold collection may be priced higher than the other collections.

....

....

....

[2]

[Total 4 marks]

Theme 2: Topic 2.2 — Making Marketing Decisions

Pricing Strategies

Warm-Up

Circle true or false for each of the statements below.

A business that doesn't have much competition may
charge higher prices for its products.   true / false

All businesses use pricing strategies that mean
they will make a profit on each product sold.   true / false

A lower price will make a product more appealing to a mass market.   true / false

1   Read the following information carefully and answer the questions that follow.

ElectricPages Ltd. is a company that sells e-reading devices and e-books. Their newest device is
the "EezyReadr", a new type of e-reading device for reading electronic books. The EezyReadr
uses a special type of e-paper which reflects natural light like normal paper. However, unlike
other e-readers on the market, the EezyReadr uses e-paper which is in full colour.
E-readers can be used to store many different electronic books. Users purchasing an EezyReadr
also create an account which allows them to purchase electronic books and magazines from
ElectricPages Ltd.'s website. The e-books on the website can only be used with ElectricPages
Ltd.'s devices, and the new EezyReadr is also not compatible with e-books from other companies.
It costs £55 to make one EezyReadr. The price of other e-reading devices on the market range
from £60-£300. Individual e-books are cheap to produce. The company sell e-books at a price
that is 70% greater than the cost of producing them.

a) The average unit cost for ElectricPages Ltd. of producing an e-book is £4.40.
    Calculate the price ElectricPages Ltd. will charge for each e-book.
    Show your working.

Price = £ ....
[2]

b) ElectricPages Ltd. is considering the following pricing strategies to establish the EezyReadr on
    the market:

    Option 1: Setting the price of an EezyReadr below the cost of making it.

    Option 2: Charging a high price for the EezyReadr when it is first released.

    Justify which **one** of these two options ElectricPages Ltd. should choose.
    Write your answer on a separate piece of paper.

[9]

[Total 11 marks]

Exam Practice Tip

You never know what might come up in a context, so be prepared for some unfamiliar material. Remember, you're not
being tested on, e.g. how much you know about e-readers, instead you just need to be able to use your own knowledge of
pricing strategies as best you can for a given context. Make sure you're confident on how to structure long answers too.

Methods of Promotion

Match each advertisement on the left with the type of market it is targeting on the right. Each type of market can only be selected **once**.

An advert in a prime time TV show   A market in a particular location

An advert in a local newspaper   A market of a particular age

An advert in a magazine for teenagers   A mass market

1   Explain **one** reason why a company will match the branding of a new product to the company's overall brand image.

....

....

....

....

[Total 3 marks]

2   Read the following information carefully and answer the questions that follow.

Mamo Ltd. is an established company which makes food and drink products. One year it launches a new brand of energy drink for sports. It decides to celebrate the launch of its new product by sponsoring a marathon running event in a major UK city.

a) Outline how sponsorship of an event by a business works.

....

....

....

[2]

b) Outline **one** reason why Mamo Ltd. may have chosen to sponsor the marathon instead of another kind of event.

....

....

....

[2]

[Total 4 marks]

3   Discuss how a business may use technology to promote its products to specific market segments.

....

....

....

....

....

....

....

....

....

....

[Total 6 marks]

4   Read the following information carefully and answer the question that follows.

> Bethany owns a luxury catering company, Beth's Kitchen. The business has very well qualified chefs and it caters for weddings and other formal events. Bethany recently exhibited at a wedding show with some of the members of her team. While at the wedding show, they gave out free samples of food to customers, along with flyers that showed the different packages offered by the company. She also offered a discount to customers who booked with the company while at the show.

Analyse the impact of Bethany using a special offer at the wedding show on Beth's Kitchen.

....

....

....

....

....

....

....

....

....

[Total 6 marks]

Exam Practice Tip

There's quite a lot to remember for promotion — that's because there are so many different ways of doing it. To make things easier, just think about the types of promotion that you see around you every day — when it's used, what for, etc.

Place

1 Which of the following describes what is meant by an e-tailer? Put a cross (✗) in **one** correct box.

A a company that sells products in a store ☐

B a customer who buys products online ☐

C a company that sells to a global market ☐

D a company that sells products online ☐

[Total 1 mark]

2 Read the following information carefully and answer the questions that follow.

Lisa owns a business which sells soft furnishings for houses. She sells her products mainly through high-street retailers. She is considering whether or not to sell her products through a number of online companies as well. The online companies that she is considering selling through have offered to buy her products for the same amount of money as the high-street retailers, but can sell them to customers at a lower overall price.

a) Define the term 'retailer'.

....

....

[1]

b) Outline **one** advantage of selling through high-street retailers rather than selling online.

....

....

....

[2]

c) Outline **one** reason why the online companies may be able to sell Lisa's products for a lower price than the high-street retailers.

....

....

....

[2]

d) Outline **one** advantage to Lisa of selling her products through online companies, apart from being able to offer a lower price to customers.

....

....

....

[2]

[Total 7 marks]

Methods of Production

Warm-Up

Warm-Up

Put the different goods listed on the left into the correct column of the table below, according to whether or not it would be best to make them via job or flow production.

personalised birthday cakes

designer clothes

pencils

chocolate bars

tailored suits

cars

Job production	Flow production

1   Which of the following describes the term 'job production'?
Put a cross (X) in **one** correct box.

A   When a firm manufactures unique products one at a time. ☐

B   When a firm produces items in a way that keeps stock levels to a minimum. ☐

C   When a firm produces items in a way that results in
buffer stocks of items at every stage in the process. ☐

D   When a firm manufactures identical products on an assembly line. ☐

[Total 1 mark]

2   Which **two** of the following are disadvantages of using flow production
to produce goods? Put a cross (X) in the **two** correct boxes.

A   It can take a long time to make each product. ☐

B   The firm may need a lot more space to store products. ☐

C   The firm may have high wage bills in order to pay skilled workers. ☐

D   The firm may need to spend a lot of money on equipment. ☐

E   The firm may have higher unit costs, as they won't be able to buy materials in bulk. ☐

[Total 2 marks]

3   Explain **one** advantage of a firm using batch production, rather than job production.

....

....

....

....

[Total 3 marks]

Working with Suppliers

1 Which of the following defines 'logistics'?
Put a cross (✗) in **one** correct box.

A   Finding and buying things that a firm needs from suppliers outside the firm. ☐

B   Getting goods and services from one part of the supply chain to another. ☐

C   Making sure a business uses as few resources as
possible and creates as little waste as possible. ☐

D   Making sure everyone in a firm takes responsibility for the quality of their work. ☐

[Total 1 mark]

2 Read the following information carefully and answer the questions that follow.

> Shake it Up is a company that makes milkshakes and delivers them to cafés across the UK.
> Shake it Up buys the milk for its milkshakes from a local farm. The factory manager can
> confirm how much milk he would like for the following day up to 6pm the day before.
> The farm always ensures that the order is ready for collection by Shake it Up's driver the next
> morning. The produce from the farm is of a high standard, so Shake it Up has been buying
> from the farm for many years. Recently, the farm has started to offer Shake it Up a discount on
> orders over £4000. Shake it Up buys enough to use this discount approximately once a week.

a) Outline **one** way that having well-managed logistics could benefit Shake it Up.

....

....

[2]

> The directors of Shake it Up have decided to grow the business by making ice cream as
> well as milkshakes. As the product is new, they aren't sure what the demand will be.
> They are considering whether to use the same arrangement for buying and collecting
> cream from the farm as for milk, or whether to use Ribblethwaites, a larger farming
> corporation that they have not used before. Buying cream from Ribblethwaites would be
> cheaper than the local farm, but would mean Shake it Up had to order cream a week in
> advance. The cream would then be delivered to Shake it Up's factory free of charge.

b) Justify whether Shake it Up should buy cream from the local farm or from Ribblethwaites.
Write your answer on a separate piece of paper.

[9]

[Total 11 marks]

Exam Practice Tip

Choosing the right supplier, working well with suppliers and then managing the rest of the supply chain effectively will all affect the costs and efficiency of a business. And don't forget that sometimes businesses may have to make a compromise in one part of the supply chain, e.g. in the costs of raw materials, to make sure the rest of the process runs smoothly.

Theme 2: Topic 2.3 — Making Operational Decisions   ☺ ☐

Quality

1 Explain **one** way in which quality assurance can help a firm to control its costs.

....

....

....

....

[Total 3 marks]

2 Read the following information carefully and answer the question that follows.

Saif runs SB Vans, a courier company that delivers furniture from factories to customers' homes. Saif guarantees delivery within 48 hours of the customer ordering their furniture. He will also set up the furniture for no extra cost.

Recently, SB Vans bought another courier company. This meant that there were many more new employees for the company. **Figure 1** shows how long it took for furniture to be delivered to customers in the month before and the month after the business began employing the new employees.

Figure 1

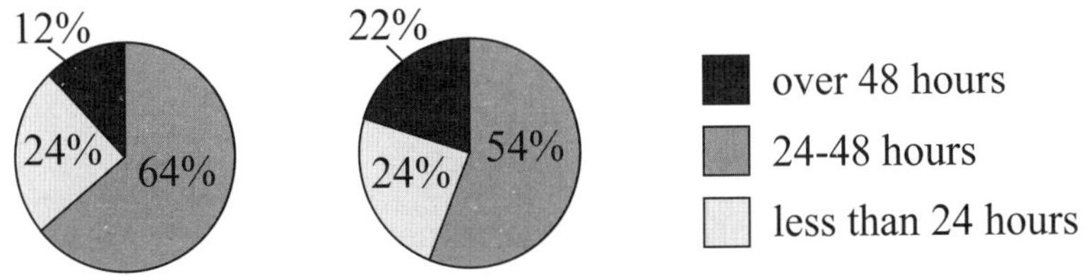

12% 24% 64%
22% 24% 54%

■ over 48 hours
■ 24-48 hours
□ less than 24 hours

1 month before the new employees started

1 month after the new employees started

Analyse how the effect the new employees have had on quality may impact SB Vans.

....

....

....

....

....

....

....

....

[Total 6 marks]

Theme 2: Topic 2.3 — Making Operational Decisions

The Sales Process

Put the following parts of the sales process in order from earliest to latest.

Approaching customers.   Finding customers.   Getting the customer to buy the item.

Presenting the product   Following up with the   Assessing customer needs.
to a customer.   customer after the sale.

1. .... earliest

2. ....

3. ....

4. ....

5. ....

6. .... latest

---

1 Which **two** of the following are forms of post-sales service?
Put a cross (✗) the **two** correct boxes.

A   Training customers in how to use the product.   ☐

B   Getting the contact details of potential customers.   ☐

C   Providing customers with information about the product they're interested in.   ☐

D   Calling customers to find out if they're interested in a product.   ☐

E   Servicing the product throughout its lifespan.   ☐

[Total 2 marks]

2 Explain how an increase in a firm's spending on
customer service can lead to an increase in profits.

....

....

....

....

[Total 3 marks]

3 Read the following information carefully and answer the questions that follow.

Bee's Travel is a company that sells luggage over the phone and via its website. When new telesales staff are hired, they are given training in the products that Bee's Travel sells. At the end of their training period, they are given a short test about the products, and given further training if they don't score over 75%. Bee's Travel aims to answer all enquiries via the website within 24 hours of receiving them, and employs two members of staff who's job is to answer website enquiries.

Recently, Bee's Travel received a complaint via their website. The complaint, and the response that Bee's Travel sent, are shown in **Figure 1**.

Figure 1

| **Damaged suitcase**
Sent: Thurs 09/03/2017 21:07

Hello there,
I recently ordered a suitcase (order reference XLD-54671). However when it arrived, the packaging was damaged, and the fabric on the outside of the suitcase was ripped.
I have attached a photo to show the damage.
Please could you send me a replacement.
Many thanks
Eliza Tandoh | **Re: Damaged suitcase**
Sent: Fri 10/03/2017 15:12

Dear Ms Tandoh,
We are very sorry to hear that your delivery did not arrive as you expected. We can assure you that this is a one off. If you return the item, we will send you another. All our items are checked before they leave our warehouse, so it must have been damaged by our courier service.
Apologies again,
Matthew Fields
Customer service assistant |

a) State **one** thing Bee's Travel does to ensure its sales process is efficient.

....

[1]

b) Outline **one** impact on Bee's Travel of training its staff to have excellent product knowledge.

....

....

....

[2]

c) Outline **one** way in which Bee's Travel could improve how it responds to customer feedback.

....

....

....

[2]

[Total 5 marks]

Exam Practice Tip

If customers don't like a company, they won't buy their products, and they're likely to tell their friends not to as well. So knowing how to please customers with good customer service is important for companies, as well as for your exams.

      Theme 2: Topic 2.3 — Making Operational Decisions

Business Calculations

1   A business makes £400 000 in revenue in one year. Its total cost of sales is £150 000 and it spends £200 000 on its remaining expenses.   (MATHS SKILLS)

a) Define the term 'net profit'.

....

....

[1]

b) Calculate the net profit for the business.
Show your working.

net profit = ...

[4]

[Total 5 marks]

2   A catering company has a sales revenue of £3m and a gross profit of £690 000. The cost of its operating expenses (other than cost of sales) and interest are £510 000.   (MATHS SKILLS)

a) Calculate the gross profit margin for the company.
Show your working.

gross profit margin = ...%

[2]

b) Calculate the net profit margin for the company.
Show your working.

net profit margin = ...%

[4]

c) A year later, the company calculates its gross profit margin to be 25% and its net profit margin to be 4%. Outline why the company may have decided to find cheaper insurance, based on this information.

....

....

[2]

d) Outline how reducing the money spent on insurance would affect the company's gross profit margin.

....

....

[2]

[Total 10 marks]

3   Explain the impact of increasing prices on the gross profit margin of a firm if costs stay the same.

....

....

....

....

....

[Total 3 marks]

4   Read the following information carefully and answer the questions that follow.

Speedy Wheels is a courier company that delivers items in parts of the United Kingdom. Speedy Wheels is considering investing £200 000 in new delivery vans. It predicts that these vans will last for approximately five years before they will need to be replaced.

The managers of Speedy Wheels forecast the increase in profit as a result of the new vans in the five years following this investment. Their results are shown in **Figure 1** below.

Figure 1

	Year 1	Year 2	Year 3	Year 4	Year 5
additional profit (£000)	170	130	150	150	120

a) Use the information above to calculate the average rate of return of the delivery vans.
    Show your working.

average rate of return = ...
[4]

b) Outline how the predicted average rate of return may affect Speedy Wheels' profits.

....

....

[2]

[Total 6 marks]

Exam Practice Tip

There are a few different steps that you have to remember when calculating the average rate of return on an investment. Make sure you don't miss one of them out — e.g. first you need to calculate the net profit, then divide this by the total number of years you are looking at to find the average annual profit. Then you need to use the equation for ARR.

Theme 2: Topic 2.4 — Making Financial Decisions

Business Data and Performance

1 Which of the following are types of market data?
Put a cross (✗) in **two** correct boxes.

A   the market share of different companies   ☐

B   customer opinions on products   ☐

C   the average rate of return on a business investment   ☐

D   how the prices of competitor products have changed   ☐

E   the gross profit margin of a business   ☐

[Total 2 marks]

2 Read the following information carefully and answer the questions that follow.

Jackie has a business which makes snacks for cafes and shops in the UK, called Jack's Snacks. Jackie decides to research the financial performance of her business in 2016 compared to previous years. She analyses how the revenue of Jack's Snacks has changed over four years. Her results are shown in **Figure 1** on the right.

Figure 1

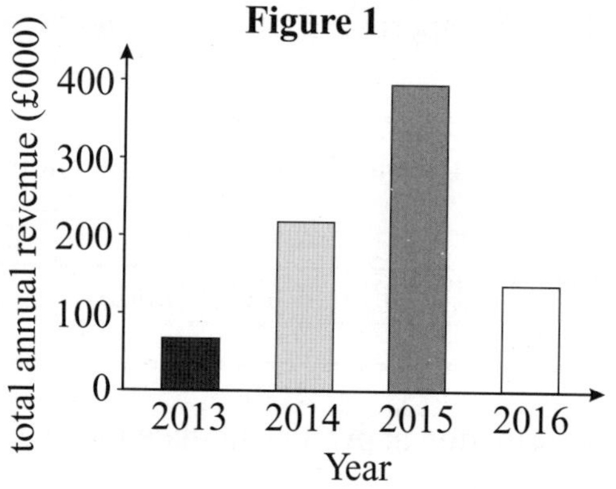

total annual revenue (£000) vs *Year* bar chart showing values at 2013, 2014, 2015, 2016.

a) Identify the largest annual revenue that Jack's Snacks made over the four years shown in **Figure 1**.

....

[1]

b) State **one** other type of financial data that Jackie may decide to collect in order to analyse the performance of her business over time.

....

[1]

c) Outline **one** limitation of using the change in revenue of Jack's Snacks in order to analyse its financial performance in 2016.

....

....

[2]

[Total 4 marks]

Internal Organisational Structures

Draw circles to show whether the statements below are **true** or **false**.

1) The number of people in each layer of a hierarchical structure generally decreases as you move up the hierarchy. **TRUE / FALSE**

2) Small firms tend to have flatter organisational structures than large firms. **TRUE / FALSE**

3) Team leaders are found at the top of a hierarchical structure. **TRUE / FALSE**

4) As a firm's organisational structure becomes hierarchical, it loses layers of management. **TRUE / FALSE**

1 Which of these statements describes the role of operational staff in a firm? Put a cross (✗) in **one** correct box.

    A   They are responsible for the business's strategy. ☐

    B   They usually look after small teams of other staff. ☐

    C   They manage team leaders. ☐

    D   They are often given specific tasks to perform by team leaders. ☐

[Total 1 mark]

2 Explain **one** disadvantage to a firm of having a centralised structure.

....

....

....

....

[Total 3 marks]

3 Explain **one** advantage to a firm of having a hierarchical structure rather than a flat structure.

....

....

....

....

[Total 3 marks]

4 Read the following information carefully and answer the questions that follow.

> Houghton & Son Ltd. make light fittings for homes. When the business started it had one small store in the owners' home town and a flat organisational structure. Now the business has a head office and a chain of stores across the country. Part of the firm's hierarchy is shown in **Figure 1**.
>
> The firm is planning to decentralise its structure, but some of the owners are reluctant to make this change.

Houghton & Son Ltd.
Claire Wilkinson UK Sales Director
↓
Andrew Gibson Regional Sales Manager
↓
Anjali Bhat District Sales Manager
↓
James Lake Branch Sales Manager
↓
Liam McNulty Branch Sales Supervisor
↓
Omar Maarouf Salesperson

Figure 1

a) State **one** responsibility that Claire Wilkinson is likely to have in her role.

....

....

[1]

b) State **one** characteristic of a flat organisational structure.

....

[1]

c) Outline **one** reason why Houghton & Son Ltd employed more managers as the company grew.

....

....

[2]

d) Analyse the impact on Houghton & Son Ltd. of decentralising its structure.

....

....

....

....

....

....

....

....

[6]

[Total 10 marks]

Exam Practice Tip

Make sure you know what it means if an organisational structure is described as being flat, hierarchical, centralised or decentralised. You should also be able to explain why certain structures are suited to some businesses better than others.

Communication

1 Explain **one** reason why effective communication in a business is important.

....

....

....

[Total 3 marks]

2 Read the following information carefully and answer the questions that follow.

> White Days are a firm that manufacture goods, such as washing machines and tumble driers. The firm has manufacturing sites in the UK, the USA and Germany.
>
> One of the main products made at the UK site is washing machines. One year the firm decided to change one of its suppliers. This meant that the screws that it was ordering were smaller than the screws from the original supplier. Shortly after this change, assembly line staff in the UK were unable to use the new screws to fasten hinges onto washing machine doors securely. The assembly line supervisor told the workers to carry on using the remaining supplies of their old, larger screws to solve the problem in the short-term.
>
> Two days later, managers of the UK site visited the factory floor and told workers operating the drilling machine to drill smaller holes for the new screws. Before long, workers fitting the hinges noticed that the screws they were now using were too big to fit the holes that were being drilled. The assembly line supervisor told workers operating the drilling machine to drill bigger holes again. The workers were reluctant to do this as they were following the managers' instructions.
>
> Three months earlier the site in Germany had encountered the same problem from using the same new screw supplier for its tumble driers, but had solved the problem straight away.

a) State **one** barrier to communication within White Days.

....

[1]

b) Analyse the likely impact of insufficient communication on White Days.

....

....

....

....

....

....

....

....

[6]

[Total 7 marks]

Theme 2: Topic 2.5 — Making Human Resource Decisions

Ways of Working

1 Which of the following describes a part-time contract of employment? Put a cross (✗) in **one** correct box.

    A   It means the employee generally works between 35 and 40 hours per week. ☐

    B   It means the employee doesn't have to accept any work that is offered to them. ☐

    C   It means the employee generally works between 10 and 30 hours per week. ☐

    D   It is only for a fixed period of time, e.g. six months. ☐

[Total 1 mark]

2 Read the following information carefully and answer the questions that follow.

> Greta Designs is a graphic design company which designs logos. When the company first started, clients would visit the firm's offices to discuss ideas for their logos and watch as the designers sketched ideas. The client would return several days later to agree on a finished design.
>
> These days, clients complete an enquiry form on the firm's website to outline their design needs. One of the graphic designers then takes on the project and uses computer software to come up with several designs, which they email to the client. The client can then give feedback on the designs via email, an instant messaging service or video call. Greta Designs employs eight permanent graphic designers, who work flexibly. Some designers choose to work from the company's office, but most of the designers work from home.
>
> Jen is a self-employed graphic designer. She has been recruited to work for Greta Designs for a specific project which she carries out in addition to commissions from other companies.

a) State **one** way in which Greta Designs' permanent graphic designers may work flexibly.

....

[1]

b) State what kind of working contract Jen has with Greta Designs.

....

[1]

c) Analyse the positive impact of technology on ways of working at Greta Designs.

....

....

....

....

....

....

....

....

[6]

[Total 8 marks]

Recruitment

1 Which of the following things would be included in a
job description? Put crosses (✗) in the **two** correct boxes.

    A   The skills needed for the job. ☐

    B   The main purpose of the job. ☐

    C   The formal title of the job. ☐

    D   The experience needed for the job. ☐

    E   The qualifications needed for the job. ☐

[Total 2 marks]

2 Read the following information carefully and answer the questions that follow.

> Jasmine owns Calm Days — a chain of beauty salons. She currently has a vacancy for a nail technician in one of her salons. She is looking for someone who already has some experience in a similar role and who will fit into the chatty, informal environment of her salons. She has advertised the vacancy on an employment website and has had lots of people applying for the job. She has made a shortlist of the candidates she is going to invite for an interview.

a) State **one** document Jasmine may have asked candidates to send to her in order to apply
for the job.

....

[1]

b) State **one** disadvantage of recruiting externally rather than internally.

....

[1]

c) Outline **one** reason why Jasmine may have decided to recruit externally rather than internally.

....

....

....

[2]

d) Jasmine didn't include a person specification in her advert.
Outline **one** reason why it may have been useful to include one.

....

....

....

[2]

[Total 6 marks]

Training and Development

Circle the examples of **formal** training below.

Warehouse staff are sent on a course so they can gain a forklift truck licence.

A bank assistant attends a college course to gain mortgage advisor qualifications.

Trainee chefs work alongside qualified chefs in a hotel kitchen.

A website designer is shown how to use a new piece of software by a colleague.

A call centre worker listens to several colleagues taking calls before they answer calls themselves.

Care workers are taught sign language by a tutor from the British Deaf Association.

1   Explain **one** benefit to a business of using informal training.

....

....

....

[Total 3 marks]

2   Read the following information carefully and answer the questions that follow.

> Peckers is a firm that makes electrical components. They have recently invested £2 million in a project to modernise their warehouse. The money invested was spent on new technology that locates and picks items that have been ordered, a warehouse extension, the recruitment of a new warehouse manager and retraining for existing warehouse staff.

a)   State **one** reason why part of the money Peckers invested in its project was spent on retraining existing warehouse staff.

....

[1]

> One of the roles of the new warehouse manager will be to conduct performance reviews for his staff. He hopes this will help the warehouse workers to be better at their jobs, which he feels could help to improve Peckers' rate of staff retention.

b)   Outline how performance reviews may help to make warehouse workers better at their jobs.

....

....

[2]

c)   Outline how training workers may improve staff retention at Peckers.

....

....

[2]

[Total 5 marks]

Motivation

1 Which of the following best describes what is meant by remuneration? Put a cross (✗) in **one** correct box.

A Payment given to employees for the work that they do. ☐

B A lump sum of money added onto payment once a year. ☐

C Giving an employee a higher position in the business. ☐

D Making sure employees meet their performance targets. ☐

[Total 1 mark]

2 Read the following information carefully and answer the questions that follow.

O_2 is a large telecommunications firm. Employees of O_2 can get fringe benefits such as discounts off O_2 products for themselves and their friends and family, discounts off gym memberships and high street shopping discount vouchers.

a) Define the term 'fringe benefits'.

....

[1]

b) Outline why O_2 gives its employees fringe benefits.

....

....

[2]

[Total 3 marks]

3 Discuss how a firm can use non-financial methods to motivate its employees.

....

....

....

....

....

....

....

....

....

....

[Total 6 marks]

4 Read the following information carefully and answer the questions that follow.

> Packman's Glazing is a business that sells doors and windows. They pay their junior sales staff an annual salary of £15 000. On top of their salary, sales staff also get 5% commission on each sale they make.
>
> Managers give junior sales staff the contact details of customers that have enquired about doors and windows and a monthly target of how many sales they should make. Junior sales staff who regularly meet their monthly targets are more likely to be promoted.
>
> In recent months, Packman's Glazing have lost two of their junior sales staff to a new, rival firm. One of the factors that persuaded the staff to move was the rival firm's pay scheme. They don't pay sales commission, but they pay junior sales staff an annual salary of £24 000.

a) State **one** method of financial motivation used by Packman's Glazing.

....

[1]

b) Define the term 'promotion'.

....

[1]

c) Drew is a junior salesman at Packman's Glazing.
In March his sales totalled £19 000 and his income from his salary before tax was £1250.
Calculate the total amount that Drew would have been paid in March before tax.
Show your working.

£ ....
[2]

d) The owners of Packman's Glazing are considering two options for how they pay their sales staff.

Option 1: Stay with their current pay scheme.

Option 2: Pay their staff a salary of £24,000 and remove commission.

Justify which **one** of these two options Packman's Glazing should choose.

Write your answer on a separate piece of paper.

[9]

[Total 13 marks]

Exam Practice Tip

Don't worry if you get given information in the exam about a method of motivation that you haven't heard of before. Just remember, motivational methods all have the same, basic outcome — they make workers feel more valued, better rewarded and generally happier to go to work each day. This can make workers more productive and less likely to leave.

Theme 2: Topic 2.5 — Making Human Resource Decisions

Mixed Questions

1   Which of the following is an example of advertising?
    Put a cross (✗) in **one** correct box.

    A   a strong brand image   ☐

    B   special offers for products   ☐

    C   selling products online   ☐

    D   posters   ☐

[Total 1 mark]

2   Which of the following statements about batch production
    are true? Put a cross (✗) in **two** correct boxes.

    A   Batch production means making products in limited quantities.   ☐

    B   Batch production is the same thing as job production.   ☐

    C   Unit costs will be higher for batch production than for job production.   ☐

    D   Batch production means making products one at a time.   ☐

    E   Each product in a batch is identical.   ☐

[Total 2 marks]

3   Which of the following describes what is meant by
    a franchisee? Put a cross (✗) in **one** correct box.

    A   An unincorporated business with one owner.   ☐

    B   A business that pays to sell the products or use the trademarks of another firm.   ☐

    C   A business that allows other businesses to sell its products under its name.   ☐

    D   An incorporated business where shares can only be sold if all the shareholders agree.   ☐

[Total 1 mark]

4   **Figure 1** below shows the annual revenue for a business over 5 years.
    Calculate the average annual revenue over this time.
    Show your working.

Year	1	2	3	4	5
Revenue (£)	15 000	17 500	16 800	19 300	21 250

Figure 1

average annual revenue = £ ....

[Total 2 marks]

Mixed Questions

10   Read the following information carefully and answer the questions that follow.

Diggitup Ltd. are a company who make gardening equipment. They manufacture and sell their products in the UK using 'just-in-time' stock control.

Their best-selling product is the SpadeAce — a tool that can be used as a spade, a fork and a hoe. Before 2007, they only sold the SpadeAce through specialist garden centres. In 2007, demand for the SpadeAce increased rapidly as more people became interested in protecting the environment by growing their own fruit and vegetables. Largely due to these changing trends, in 2007 Diggitup Ltd. saw their total revenue grow to £800 000, giving them a net profit of £164 000. To meet the increased demand for the SpadeAce, the company took out a £250 000 loan so that they could buy some new machinery, which would allow them to increase their output.

The company also wanted to change their marketing mix to meet the new demand. In 2008, Diggitup Ltd. decided to find new places to sell their products to target people who gardened as a hobby. They looked at the sales figures of Maxi Store, a large supermarket chain. The diagrams in **Figure 2** show the sales of non-food products at Maxi Store in the years 2005 and 2007.

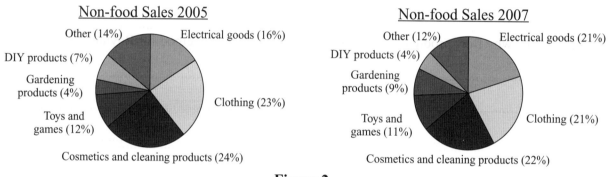

Figure 2

Diggitup Ltd. decided to try to sell their products through Maxi Store. The supermarket ordered £400 000 worth of the SpadeAce in 2008, which meant that Diggitup had to make more than double the number of SpadeAces than they had in the previous year.

Many of Diggitup Ltd.'s raw materials come from China. As its output increased, Diggitup Ltd. found that some of their larger wood deliveries were of worse quality than before, and arrived after the delivery date. They investigated new suppliers for the wood and after much consideration, in 2012 Diggitup Ltd. decided to buy their wood from a UK supplier. The supplier is more expensive than their Chinese supplier, but unlike the Chinese supplier, the wood it provides is certified as being sustainable. Since changing suppliers, the deliveries have been consistently on time.

a) State what type of growth Diggitup Ltd. are undertaking.

....

[1]

b) Outline the method of 'just-in-time stock control'.

....

....

[2]

c) Outline **one** way Diggitup Ltd. benefits from globalisation.

....

....

....

[2]

d) In 2006, Diggitup Ltd.'s net profit margin was 18.2%.
Calculate the difference in the net profit margin between 2006 and 2007.
Show your working.

difference in profit margins = ... %

[3]

e) **Figure 3** below shows the effect that Diggitup Ltd. predict the
new machinery will have on their profits over the course of its 8 year lifespan.
Calculate the average rate of return for the new machinery.
Show your working.

Year	1	2	3	4	5	6	7	8
Increased profit (£)	120 000	190 000	210 000	230 000	240 000	235 000	215 000	160 000

Figure 3

average rate of return = ... %

[4]

f) Analyse the impact that selling the SpadeAce at branches of Maxi Store might
have had on Diggitup Ltd.

....

....

....

....

....

....

....

[6]

g) Evaluate whether changing wood supplier would have been beneficial for Diggitup Ltd.
Use the information provided, as well as your knowledge of business.
Write your answer on a separate piece of paper.

[12]

[Total 30 marks]

11 Read the following information carefully and answer the questions that follow.

In 2006, Richard and Harry took out an £8000 loan to set up their partnership, Clear Skin, a business selling natural skincare products over the internet.

After researching the market, they decided to launch two products — a cleanser that reduces acne, aimed at teenagers, and a moisturiser aimed at reducing wrinkles in over 50s. They did some research to see how their company compared to some of their competitors. A summary of this research is shown in **Figure 4** below.

Figure 4

Company	Average price of products	Number of different products sold	Quality of products
Clear Skin	£18	2	high
Super Balm	£14	42	high
Skin Easy	£6	13	low
Pore Perfect	£12	20	medium

Richard and Harry aimed for their business to have achieved financial security within 5 years of starting, by focusing on increasing their market share and sales during this period. They planned to buy their aloe vera from an Indian supplier, and aimed to reinvest some of their profits into education in the areas the aloe vera came from. Their other aims included using natural ingredients in all their products and paying a fair price for the ingredients.

There were significant economic changes in the years following 2007:
* At the start of 2008, the UK unemployment rate was 5.2%.
  This figure had risen to 7.8% by the end of 2009.
* At the start of 2008, the Bank of England base rate for interest was 5.5%.
  This figure had fallen to 0.5% by the end of 2009.
* At the start of 2008, the exchange rate of the British pound against the Indian currency, the rupee, was 78.2. This figure had fallen to 75.3 by the end of 2009.

a) State **one** other suitable source of finance that Richard and Harry could have used to start their business.

....

[1]

b) Outline the difference between the ownership of a sole trader business and of a partnership.

....

....

[2]

c) Outline **one** reason why Richard and Harry's market research needed to be reliable.

....

....

....

[2]

d) Outline **one** way in which Richard and Harry have used market segmentation.

....

....

....

[2]

e) Outline **one** weakness of the company Skin Easy compared to Clear Skin.

....

....

....

[2]

f) Outline how Clear Skin's aims will benefit **one** of their stakeholders.

....

....

....

[2]

g) Richard and Harry will repay their loan in 48 monthly installments of £200.
Calculate the interest on the loan.
Show your working.

interest = ... %

[3]

h) One year after opening, Harry and Richard were looking at ways to increase their market share.
They had two options:

Option 1: Set up a social media account.
Option 2: Increase their product range.

Justify which **one** of these options Richard and Harry should have chosen.
Write your answer on a separate piece of paper.

[9]

i) Evaluate whether Clear Skin is likely to have benefitted from the changing economic climate.
You should use the information provided, as well as your knowledge of business.
Write your answer on a separate piece of paper.

[12]

[Total 35 marks]

Mixed Questions

Answers

Note on Answers:

A lot of the time in Business, there isn't really a "right answer". Instead, it's about being able to explain yourself and justify your decisions.

Pages 5-6 — Enterprise

1   B *[1 mark]*

2   E.g. the business may make a large profit *[1 mark]*. This could mean the entrepreneur earns more money than they did before they started the business *[1 mark]*, which could give them a better quality of life *[1 mark]*.

3   E.g. building a good brand image can add value to a product *[1 mark]*. This is because customers will recognise the brand as being trustworthy/desirable *[1 mark]*, so may be willing to spend more on products with that brand *[1 mark]*.

4   How to grade your answer:
Level 0: Nothing worthy of credit. *[No marks]*
Level 1: There is some attempt to describe some changes which may cause business ideas, but with little discussion of the reasons why these changes cause business ideas to come about. *[1 to 2 marks]*
Level 2: A number of different changes that can cause business ideas have been described, with some discussion of the reasons why these changes cause business ideas to come about. *[3 to 4 marks]*
Level 3: There is a detailed description of the different changes that can cause business ideas, and a clear discussion of the reasons why these changes cause business ideas to come about. *[5 to 6 marks]*
Here are some points your answer may include:
Over time, technology changes or new technology is invented.
New business ideas can come about that use this new technology.
Over time, there are changes in what customers want.
Some new business ideas come about in order to provide for these new wants.
Sometimes, a good or service will become obsolete. Owners of businesses that offer these goods or services will have to come up with new ideas so that their businesses survive.

5   How to grade your answer:
Level 0: Nothing worthy of credit. *[No marks]*
Level 1: There is some attempt to describe the different responsibilities that an entrepreneur might need to fulfil, but with little discussion of the reasons why fulfilling these responsibilities is important for running a new business. *[1 to 2 marks]*
Level 2: There is a description of a number of different responsibilities that an entrepreneur might need to fulfil, with some discussion of the reasons why fulfilling these responsibilities is important for running a new business. *[3 to 4 marks]*

Level 3: There is a detailed description of the different responsibilities that an entrepreneur would need to fulfil, and a clear discussion of the reasons why fulfilling these responsibilities is important for running a new business. *[5 to 6 marks]*
Here are some points your answer may include:
Entrepreneurs need to be willing to take risks.
There are lots of unknowns involved in running a new business, such as investing money that might be lost if the business fails.
Even though an entrepreneur can write a business plan before they start, they can't know exactly what will happen, so they need to be able to take calculated risks.
Entrepreneurs need to make business decisions.
There are lots of decisions to be made when running a new business, such as the business's aims, its structure, who to employ, and what to do if things go wrong.
Entrepreneurs need to be able to organise resources.
Entrepreneurs need to be able to organise the day-to-day running of the business, and should also be able to plan for the future.

6 a) Hint: make sure that you give a risk that would be faced by a business that has just started up, rather than a risk that only more established businesses might face.
E.g. if Tasty Teas doesn't make enough profit, then Louise might not be able to pay back the money she has borrowed from the bank *[1 mark]*, and her business may fail / she may lose money *[1 mark]*.

   b) Hint: the information gives two ways that Louise has added value to ready cooked meals — she has improved their quality and added a unique selling point by offering different meals to competitors. Whichever option you choose, make sure you explain why it adds value to the product.
E.g. Louise is producing meals that are higher quality than competitor products / which have ethically sourced ingredients *[1 mark]*. This means customers will be willing to pay more for ready meals from Tasty Teas as they may taste better / they may want to make sure what they buy is ethically sourced *[1 mark]*.

Page 7 — Competition

1   E.g. a business may develop high quality products in order to stay competitive *[1 mark]*, since its customers are more likely to be satisfied *[1 mark]* and will therefore be more likely to buy from the business than from its competitors *[1 mark]*.

2 a) E.g. in 2012, BlueBamboo was the only company selling a plant sensor *[1 mark]*, this will have increased its competitiveness, since customers will have only been able to buy this product from BlueBamboo / it will have made the company seem more innovative than its competitors *[1 mark]*.

b) How to grade your answer:

Level 0: Nothing written worthy of credit. *[No marks]*

Level 1: Some attempt has been made to recommend what BlueBamboo should do, but with little justification for why this is the better option. *[1 to 3 marks]*

Level 2: Some of the advantages and disadvantages to BlueBamboo of each option have been given, along with a recommendation for which option BlueBamboo should choose. There is some reasoning to the recommendation, but it is lacking in detail or not fully justified. *[4 to 6 marks]*

Level 3: There is a detailed explanation of the advantages and disadvantages of each option, with a well-reasoned and fully justified recommendation of what BlueBamboo should do. *[7 to 9 marks]*

Here are some points your answer may include:
Reducing the price of the Shoot Sense may make the product more desirable to customers since it will be closer to the price of its competitors. This may increase the sales of Shoot Sense. However, BlueBamboo would earn less money per product sold. Also, reducing the price to £90 would still mean that Shoot Sense is more expensive than all the other products on the market. So customers concerned about price may still not be likely to buy it.

BlueBamboo currently loses potential customers due to its lack of adequate customer service. By improving its customer service, visitors to its website may be more likely to buy Shoot Sense since they may be able to ask a customer services assistant about how to use it with their smartphone. Providing extra training to customers who have bought the sensor would also help to improve customer service. This would mean that customers would get more out of the different features of Shoot Sense and therefore would be more likely to be satisfied with the product. Improving the speed of delivery of Shoot Sense may also help to improve customer service and mean that the company will have fewer unhappy customers. This may increase sales in the future.

Making these changes to customer service may be expensive and therefore may increase costs for the BlueBamboo. However, knowing that BlueBamboo provides good customer service may also mean that customers will be more willing to pay more for Shoot Sense than other competitor products.

You need to finish your answer with a conclusion recommending what you think BlueBamboo should do — make sure you've looked thoroughly at all the information given. E.g. 'BlueBamboo should invest in improvements to its customer service. Investing in its customer service is likely to increase the sales of Shoot Sense and may also mean that customers will be willing to pay the high price for the product.'

Page 8 — Introduction to Market Research

1 D *[1 mark]*

2 A *[1 mark]* and C *[1 mark]*

3 a) E.g. price of the suits customers need / the quality of suits that customers need / the convenience of where the suits are sold for customers *[1 mark]*.

b) E.g. Davis and Sons can use the market research to ensure that they sell suits in colours that their customers will buy, e.g. dark green suits *[1 mark]* and so avoid spending money on suits in colours their customers won't buy *[1 mark]*.

c) E.g. by identifying a gap in the market, Davis and Sons may be able to start offering customers dark green suits before nearby competitors do *[1 mark]*. This may lead to increased revenue for the firm *[1 mark]*.

Page 9 — Types of Market Research

1 C *[1 mark]*

2 E.g. secondary market research is likely to be cheaper than primary market research *[1 mark]*, since the data is already available *[1 mark]*, which is an advantage to small businesses because they are unlikely to have as much money as larger businesses *[1 mark]*.

3 a) E.g. Best Publications should ensure that the focus groups use people from the correct market segment / teenagers *[1 mark]*, so that the information gathered is useful for the business *[1 mark]*.

b) E.g. Best Publications may collect information on what potential customers enjoy from their social media accounts *[1 mark]* and use it to see what sorts of things are popular / increasing in popularity *[1 mark]*.

c) observation *[1 mark]*

Pages 10-11 — Using Market Research

Warm-Up
quantitative, qualitative, quantitative, quantitative

1 How to grade your answer:

Level 0: Nothing worthy of credit. *[No marks]*

Level 1: Some attempt to describe the impact that the market research may have on the products that Tom's Teas offers, but with little explanation of why it may have this impact. *[1 to 2 marks]*

Level 2: There is a good description of the impact that the market research will have on the products offered by Tom's Teas, with some explanation of why it may have this impact. *[3 to 4 marks]*

Level 3: There is a detailed description of the impact that the market research will have on the products offered by Tom's Teas, and a clear explanation of why it may have this impact. *[5 to 6 marks]*

Here are some points your answer may include:
Tom may be interested in selling the jasmine deluxe tea in his shop, since this was the most popular tea on his questionnaire.

He will probably choose not to sell his liquorice and mint tea since it had a very low popularity of only 4% and many respondents had a strong dislike of the tea and thought that it tasted bitter.

He is also unlikely to sell the camomile and nettle tea since it also had a low popularity of only 10%. Despite the fact that there were few complaints about this tea, it is unlikely that he would sell enough of the tea for it to be worth his while blending and selling it.

A majority of respondents to the questionnaire stated that they would be unlikely to order one of the three teas instead of another drink in his shop. Therefore it would only be worth blending and selling the jasmine deluxe tea since it was the most popular and he is unlikely to sell many of these new teas anyway.

2 a) How to grade your answer:

Level 0: Nothing worthy of credit. *[No marks]*

Level 1: Some attempt to describe the impact that changing the flyers will have on the RiverHouse Restaurant, but with little explanation of why the changes are likely to have this impact. *[1 to 2 marks]*

Level 2: There is a good description of the impact that changing the flyers could have on the RiverHouse Restaurant, with some explanation of why the changes are likely to have this impact . *[3 to 4 marks]*

Level 3: There is a detailed description of the impact that changing the flyers is likely to have on the RiverHouse Restaurant, and a clear explanation of why the changes are likely to have this impact. *[5 to 6 marks]*

Here are some points your answer may include:

The original flyers prioritised showing the location and prices of the restaurant.

However, the market research data shows that for all but a few customers, location is not the most important aspect of the restaurant.

In addition, only 25% of respondents said price was the most important aspect of the restaurant in 2012, and this had dropped to 16% by 2017.

The new flyers prioritise the atmosphere of the restaurant, by showing an image of the inside and advertising music events that she is holding.

In 2017, atmosphere was the most popular response for the most important aspect of the restaurant.

The percentage of respondents who said atmosphere was most important increased between 2012 and 2017. So by promoting the atmosphere of the restaurant, the new flyers are likely to appeal to more customers than the original flyers. So more customers are likely to visit the restaurant and its sales are likely to increase.

b) How to grade your answer:

Level 0: Nothing worthy of credit. *[No marks]*

Level 1: Some attempt is made to recommend which improvement Georgina should make, but with little explanation for why this should be done. *[1 to 3 marks]*

Level 2: Some of the advantages and disadvantages of the different options for improving her restaurant have been given, along with a recommendation of what Georgina should do. There is some reasoning to the recommendation, but it is lacking in detail or not fully explained. *[4 to 6 marks]*

Level 3: There is a thorough description of the advantages and disadvantages of the different options for improving her restaurant, with a detailed recommendation of what Georgina should do that has been fully explained. *[7 to 9 marks]*

Here are some points your answer may include:

Improving the decorations and furniture:

Georgina's customers are likely to be more satisfied if she improves the decorations and furniture, since 42% of them said that the atmosphere of a restaurant was the most important aspect to them. This is a greater percentage than those who said that the choice of food was the most important aspect to them, so it may be more beneficial than increasing the size of the menu.

There has been an increase of 4.5% in customers saying that atmosphere is the most important aspect to them since 2012, suggesting that atmosphere is becoming more important to customers. Therefore improving the decorations and furniture may also attract new customers.

However, the atmosphere of the restaurant may be dependent on more than just the decorations and furniture. So changing these aspects of the restaurant's appearance may not necessarily affect the restaurant's atmosphere.

It may also be costly for Georgina to change the appearance of her restaurant.

Increasing the number of choices on the menu:

A high percentage of customers (39%) said that the choice of food was the most important aspect to them, so increasing the choice of food available may lead to more satisfied customers.

There has been an increase of 6.5% in customers saying that choice of food is the most important aspect for them, since 2012. This is a greater increase than for atmosphere, so the choice of food has become more important by a greater degree than atmosphere. Therefore it may be more beneficial for Georgina to increase the choice on the menu.

However, increasing the choice on the menu may affect the running of her restaurant, since her cooks will have to be able to make more dishes and she may have to buy in different ingredients.

It may also increase her costs, as she may need to purchase more types of ingredients.

You need to finish your answer with a conclusion recommending what you think Georgina should do — make sure you've looked thoroughly at all the information given. E.g. 'Georgina should improve the decorations and furniture. Although this may be costly, she is likely to have more satisfied customers and it won't affect the running of the restaurant.'

Page 12 — Market Segmentation

1 a) 1. BoogieMix

2. DustySounds *[1 mark for both parts correct.]*

b) Market segmentation is when people within a market are divided into different groups *[1 mark]*.

c) Hint: there are lots of possible answers to this question. Thinking of common ways in which a market may be segmented (e.g. by age or income) may help you to pick out an appropriate feature from the information you've been given.

E.g. individuals with a high income / individuals interested in trends in music / older people *[1 mark]*.

d) BassLine Ltd. *[1 mark]*

e) E.g. there is a gap in the market map for a moderately priced, high quality record player *[1 mark]*, so there may be high customer demand for it *[1 mark]*.

Pages 13-14 — *Business Aims and Objectives*

Warm-Up

Financial Aims	Non-financial Aims
To have sales of £30 000 To increase market share	To have the challenge of running a business To improve education in the community

1   Aims are overall goals that a business wants to achieve *[1 mark]*. Objectives are more specific targets *[1 mark]* which are used to help measure how well a business is achieving its aims *[1 mark]*.

2 a)   E.g. to have the independence/control of being able to choose the menu and ingredients used in the business *[1 mark]*.

   b)   Hint: you get one mark for stating a difference in the aims, and one mark for explaining why the aims will be different — for this part of the answer, you should try and think about the differences between the businesses. E.g. the aims of Rye Ltd. are likely to be more focused on things such as increasing market share/sales/profits, rather than survival *[1 mark]*, because Rye Ltd. is a more established company than Karen's Sarnies *[1 mark]*.

3 a)   E.g. the sales targets are measurable steps *[1 mark]* that Ole could check to see if he was on track for achieving his aim of sales over £120 000 in the eighth year *[1 mark]*.

   b)   Change in sales = 180 000 − 150 000 = £30 000
Percentage change = (30 000 ÷ 150 000) × 100
= **20%** *[2 marks for correct answer, otherwise 1 mark for correctly calculating change in sales]*

   c)   How to grade your answer:
Level 0: Nothing worthy of credit. *[No marks]*
Level 1: There is some attempt to describe the impact on Merino of Ole sticking to his aims, but with little or no analysis of the overall effect these impacts will have on the business. *[1 to 2 marks]*
Level 2: A number of impacts on Merino of Ole sticking to his aims have been described, with some analysis of the overall effect these impacts will have on the business. *[3 to 4 marks]*
Level 3: There is a detailed description of the impacts on Merino of Ole sticking to his aims, and a clear analysis of the overall effect of these impacts on the business. *[5 to 6 marks]*
Here are some points your answer may include:

Aim 1
In order to stick to his aim of making knitted garments using pure wool sourced from Scandinavia, Ole decided to decline the offer from the national department store to stock his products. This meant the business lost out on sales revenue — a predicted £30 000. This may have meant that Merino grew more slowly and that Ole couldn't invest in growing the business.

Aim 2
However, in order to stick to his aim of making £120 000 per year by the eighth year, Ole started supplying his products to a local retailer in 2011, which led to more sales revenue, on top of the sales he was already making through the website. He also decided to launch a national advertising campaign, which made people more aware of his brand, and helped towards his aim by increasing sales.
This meant by 2014, Ole had already achieved his aim in a shorter amount of time and made greater sales than hoped for — £150 000. This means that Ole could afford to turn down the offer from the national department store and still stick to his aims.

Pages 15-16 — *Revenue, Costs and Profit*

Warm-Up
You should have circled insurance and managers' salaries.

1   A *[1 mark]*

2   D *[1 mark]*

Interest = ((total repayment − borrowed amount) ÷ borrowed amount) × 100 = ((27 720 − 26 000) ÷ 26 000) × 100 = (1720 ÷ 26 000) × 100 = 6.6%

3 a)   Year 2: 450 × 7 = £3150 *[1 mark]*
Year 3: 1200 × 7 = £8400 *[1 mark]*

   b)   Year 2 *[1 mark]*

In year 2 the total money received was less than the total costs.

4 a)   The variable costs increased between 2015 and 2016 *[1 mark]* because they depend on output, and the output of the business increased during this period *[1 mark]*.

   b)   total costs = fixed costs + variable costs
2015: total costs = 40 000 + 30 000 = £70 000
2016: total costs = 40 000 + 40 000 = £80 000
change in total costs = 80 000 − 70 000 = **£10 000**
[3 marks for correct answer, otherwise 1 mark for calculating the correct total costs for 2015 and 1 mark for calculating the correct total costs for 2016.]

   c)   profit = revenue − costs
profit in 2015 = 90 000 − 30 000 − 40 000 = £20 000
profit in 2016 = 110 000 − 40 000 − 40 000 = £30 000
change in profit = 30 000 − 20 000 = £10 000
Percentage increase = (10 000 ÷ 20 000) × 100 = **50%**
[4 marks for correct answer, otherwise 1 mark for correctly calculating profit in 2015, 1 mark for correctly calculating profit in 2016, 1 mark for correctly calculating change in profit.]

   d)   variable cost per unit in 2016 = total variable costs ÷ output or quantity sold = 40 000 ÷ 12 500 = £3.20
change in variable cost per unit between 2016 and 2017 = 3.45 − 3.20 = **£0.25**
[2 marks for correct answer, otherwise 1 mark for calculating the correct variable cost per unit for 2016]

Pages 17-18 — *Break-Even Analysis*

1   A *[1 mark]*

2 a)   Break-even level of output = fixed cost ÷ (sales price − variable cost)
= 50 000 ÷ (1.80 − 0.85) = 50 000 ÷ 0.95 = 52 631.57...
= 52 600 (3 s.f.)
[2 marks for correct answer, otherwise 1 mark for using the correct equation for break-even level of output]

   b)   E.g. the firm will know how much its output can fall by before it starts to make a loss *[1 mark]*.

c) Break-even point for revenue = break-even output × sales price
= 48 000 × 1.80 = **£86 400**
[2 marks for correct answer, otherwise 1 mark for using the correct equation for the break-even point for revenue]

3 a) £1000 *[1 mark]*

b) Break-even output = 500 units *[1 mark]*
Margin of safety = 800 − 500 = 300 units *[1 mark]*

c) How to grade your answer:
Level 0: Nothing worthy of credit. *[No marks]*
Level 1: There is some attempt to describe the impact that moving to the new supplier could have had on Fully Charged Ltd., but with little explanation of the advantages and disadvantages to the firm. *[1 to 2 marks]*
Level 2: There is a good description of the impact that moving to the new supplier could have had on Fully Charged Ltd., with some explanation of the advantages and disadvantages to the firm. *[3 to 4 marks]*
Level 3: There is a detailed description of the impact that moving to the new supplier could have had on Fully Charged Ltd, and a clear explanation of the advantages and disadvantages to the firm. *[5 to 6 marks]*
Here are some points your answer may include:
An increase in variable costs of 25% per unit sold would have meant that variable costs would have increased from £2 per unit to £2.50 per unit — this is an increase of £0.50 per unit.
The change to the new supplier caused Ryan to increase the price of each charger, so revenue was £1 more for every unit sold. The changes in costs and revenue would have meant that Fully Charged Ltd. earned £0.50 (£1 − £0.50) more for every unit sold. Therefore, overall profit per unit sold would have increased.
Figure 2 shows that Fully Charged Ltd.'s break even output was 400 units in 2016, whereas Figure 1 shows that it was 500 units in 2013 when it using the original supplier. Therefore the new supplier would have meant that Fully Charged Ltd. would have to sell 100 fewer units before making a profit.
However, the increase in price of the chargers may have meant that fewer customers would be willing to buy them. Therefore making these changes could have resulted in a loss of revenue and the business's profits may not have increased as a result.

Page 19 — Cash Flow

Warm-Up
A business's cash **inflow** is the amount of money that it receives, for example through **selling** products. The cash **outflow** is the amount of money it spends, for example, through **paying** employees. When the **net** cash flow is **positive**, there is more inflow than outflow.

1 E.g. cash is the money that a business can spend immediately *[1 mark]*, so if the business doesn't have enough cash, it may not be able to pay its debts / it may become insolvent *[1 mark]* and could lead to the firm failing *[1 mark]*.

2 a) E.g. businesses can use cash flow forecasts to predict whether they will have difficulties making payments in the future *[1 mark]*, which means they can arrange additional finance if necessary for certain periods *[1 mark]*.

b) June and July *[1 mark]*
This is because it has a negative bank balance at the beginning or end of these months.

Page 20 — Cash Flow — Credit

1 a) A business's bank balance at the start of the month *[1 mark]*.

b) A business's bank balance at the end of the month *[1 mark]*.

c) August cash inflow = 1400 *[1 mark]*
To find this value, look back to the orders coming in in June — this is because these orders will be paid for after the 2 months of credit has passed.
July cash outflow = 1350 *[1 mark]*
The net cash flow is −50. So the cash outflow must be £50 more than the cash inflow, which is 1300 + 50 = 1350.
May net cash flow = −850 or (850) *[1 mark]*
The net cash flow is the cash inflow minus the cash outflow, which is 350 − 1200 = −850.
June opening balance = −250 or (250) *[1 mark]*
The opening balance for June will be the closing balance for May.
October closing balance = 1850 *[1 mark]*
To calculate the closing balance, just add up the net cash flow and the opening balance: 1100 + 750 = 1850.

d) How to grade your answer:
Level 0: Nothing worthy of credit. *[No marks]*
Level 1: There is some attempt to describe the impact of the rise in demand for sunglasses on Yoo Too Sunglasses Ltd.'s cash flow, but with little explanation of how it may cause this impact. *[1 to 2 marks]*
Level 2: There is a good description of how the rise in demand for sunglasses may impact Yoo Too Sunglasses Ltd.'s cash flow, with some explanation of how it may cause this impact. *[3 to 4 marks]*
Level 3: There is a detailed description of how the rise in demand for sunglasses may impact Yoo Too Sunglasses Ltd.'s cash flow, and a clear explanation of how it may cause this impact. *[5 to 6 marks]*
Here are some points your answer may include:
The increase in demand is likely to mean that it is advantageous for Yoo Too Sunglasses Ltd. to manufacture more sunglasses than they otherwise would have done in November.
The cash outflow for Yoo Too Sunglasses Ltd. in November might increase as the business spends more money on manufacturing more sunglasses.
This might mean that Yoo Too Sunglasses Ltd. will have to take out short-term finance to cover their costs during this period.
The cash inflow is likely to increase in the following January as the credit from customers who have bought sunglasses is paid off.
This may mean that Yoo Too Sunglasses Ltd. will find it easier to pay off their bills during this period.
As Yoo Too Sunglasses Ltd. will have extra cash in the business, they may choose to make investments

into the business in January. This might improve the business's cash flow in the future.

Page 21 — Sources of Finance — Small Businesses

1   A *[1 mark]*

2   E.g. if the business makes the payment too late, it could have to pay a large fee *[1 mark]* which would increase the costs of the business *[1 mark]* and may decrease overall profit *[1 mark]*.

3   E.g. a venture capitalist may help to fund a new, risky business if it has the potential to grow quickly *[1 mark]*, since they will get a stake in the business *[1 mark]* and will get a return on their investment more quickly than for businesses with less growth potential *[1 mark]*.

4 a)   Crowd funding is when a large number of people each contribute a small amount of money to a business *[1 mark]*.

   b)   E.g. Nadia will not have made much profit to use to fund her second year *[1 mark]* due to high costs and low revenue/sales in her first year *[1 mark]*.

Pages 22-24 — Business Ownership Structures

Warm-Up

1 true

2 true

3 false

4 false

1   B *[1 mark]*

2   Hint: there are lots of disadvantages that you could give for this question. Make sure you state and fully explain one disadvantage to get all three marks.
E.g. sole traders may have to work long hours / not get many holidays *[1 mark]*, as there may be few/no other employees in the business *[1 mark]*. This means sole traders may regularly feel tired *[1 mark]*. / Sole traders have unlimited liability *[1 mark]*, which means if the business goes bust they are legally responsible for paying back all of the business's debts *[1 mark]*, so may have to sell their possessions *[1 mark]*. / Sole traders are unincorporated *[1 mark]*, so if anyone sues the business, the sole trader is sued personally *[1 mark]*, which may mean the sole trader loses money *[1 mark]*. / It can be hard for a sole trader to raise money *[1 mark]* as banks see sole traders as risky *[1 mark]*, so it may be hard to set up/grow the business *[1 mark]*.

3   E.g. having limited liability means the shareholders aren't liable for the debts of the business if it goes bust *[1 mark]*, so their financial risk is reduced *[1 mark]* as if the business fails they will only lose the money they have invested *[1 mark]*.

4   A partnership is made up of two or more people *[1 mark]*. Each partner has an equal say in all business decisions *[1 mark]* and receives an equal share of the profits (unless they have agreed otherwise) *[1 mark]*.

5 a)   30% *[1 mark]*
The total percentage should add up to 100. So Keith Blackwell will own 100 − 30 − 25 − 15 = 30% of the company.

   b)   **How to grade your answer:**
Level 0: Nothing worthy of credit. *[No marks]*
Level 1: There is some attempt to describe the impacts on Blackwell's Pies of changing from a partnership to a private limited company, but with little explanation of the overall effect these impacts will have on the business. *[1 to 2 marks]*
Level 2: A number of impacts on Blackwell's Pies of changing from a partnership to a private limited company have been described, with some explanation of the overall effect these impacts will have on the business. *[3 to 4 marks]*
Level 3: There is a detailed description of the impacts on Blackwell's Pies of changing from a partnership to a private limited company, and a clear explanation of the overall effect of these impacts on the business. *[5 to 6 marks]*
Here are some points your answer may include:
Converting Blackwell's Pies to a private limited company means that it will have limited liability. This means that it may be easier for the business to raise money, as people may be more willing to invest if they are only risking losing the money that they have invested if the business fails. It also means that it might be easier for Blackwell's Pies to get a loan or mortgage. Having extra capital means the firm would have more money available to expand the business. Being able to expand may mean that the company makes more sales, which could lead to increased profit. Converting to a private limited company means that there are two more people who own Blackwell's Pies, so it may be more difficult for decisions to be made. Converting to a private limited company might be expensive, because of the legal paperwork required. This will increase costs for Blackwell's Pies. However, this is a one-off cost, so shouldn't reduce profits in the long-term.
Converting to a private limited company means that the accounts for Blackwell's Pies need to be published each year, which means more administration will be needed within the business. This takes time and money, so may lead to lower profits for Blackwell's Pies overall.

6   **How to grade your answer:**
Level 0: Nothing worthy of credit. *[No marks]*
Level 1: Some attempt has been made to recommend what Kate should do, but with little justification for why this should be done. *[1 to 3 marks]*
Level 2: Some of the advantages and disadvantages of Kate going into partnership have been described, along with a recommendation of what she should do. There is some reasoning to the recommendation, but it is lacking in detail or not fully justified. *[4 to 6 marks]*
Level 3: There is a detailed explanation of the advantages and disadvantages of going into business with a partner, with a well-reasoned and fully justified recommendation of what Kate should do. *[7 to 9 marks]*

84

Here are some points your answer may include:

Advantages of partnership

Kate does not have a lot of money to put into the business. Starting up with a partner will mean that there is more capital available to start the business than if she started as a sole trader.

Kate has only just qualified as an accountant. Having a partner could mean there's a broader range of skills and expertise, which could be useful for Kate as she starts her career.

Kate and her partner would be able to share work, so it would reduce the workload for Kate compared to starting a business as a sole trader.

Disadvantages of partnership

Kate would be legally responsible for the actions of the other person in the partnership, and as Kate doesn't know this person very well, this could be very risky.

The partner Kate is considering might not want to run the business in the same way as Kate. There could be disagreements if they have very different ideas about how the business should be run.

Having a partner means Kate will get a smaller share of the profits compared to if she was a sole trader.

You need to finish your answer with a conclusion recommending what you think Kate should do — make sure you've looked thoroughly at all the information given. E.g. 'Kate should start up the business on her own, rather than as half of a partnership. Even though this means she may have to work longer hours, and have less money to start with, it means that she doesn't have the risks of working with someone she doesn't know very well, and will earn a greater share of the profits.'

7 a)   A franchise is a business ownership structure where the owner pays a fee to sell products or use the trademark of another firm *[1 mark]*.

b)   How to grade your answer:

Level 0: Nothing worthy of credit. *[No marks]*

Level 1: Some advantages and disadvantages of setting up as a franchise are given, but with little explanation of whether Isaac will benefit from becoming a franchisee. *[1 to 4 marks]*

Level 2: A number of advantages and disadvantages of setting up as a franchise are described. There is some attempt to conclude whether Isaac would benefit overall from becoming a franchisee, but with little or no explanation to justify the conclusion. *[5 to 8 marks]*

Level 3: There is a detailed and thorough analysis of the advantages and disadvantages of setting up as a franchise. A conclusion has been made as to whether Isaac will benefit from becoming a franchisee, which has been fully justified using evidence. *[9 to 12 marks]*

Here are some points your answer may include:

Franchises often have rules about how the business must operate.

Isaac's business is already a dog sitting business, but he's unsure about caring for other pets.

Petpals™ franchises offer services to look after other animals as well, so becoming a franchisee may mean Isaac will have to offer services he doesn't want to.

However, Petpals™ provides training to franchisees, so Isaac may be more confident looking after animals that aren't dogs once he has been given this training.

Franchisees often have to pay money to the franchisor to set up the franchise.

Petpals™ requires an initial investment of approximately £20 000. It's possible they might also want a share of the profits that Isaac makes in later years. If Isaac invested this money into his current dog sitting business instead, he might end up making more money in the long term.

Customers may already recognise a franchisor's brand name.

Petpals™ is an established, well-regarded company. Customers may be more willing to trust Isaac if he operates under the Petpals™ name rather than as his own business. Since customers are likely to care a lot about the treatment their pets get, operating under a trusted brand name could greatly improve Isaac's sales, so his business could grow more quickly than if he continued with his existing pet boarding business.

Petpals™ would provide Isaac with support, such as training, writing a business plan and helping to set up a marketing campaign. Isaac already has experience with marketing, but might require assistance with the other aspects of his business, so this support could help to make his business more successful than it would be if he continued to operate as his own business.

You need to finish your answer with a conclusion about whether Isaac will benefit from setting up a franchise — make sure you've looked thoroughly at all the information given. E.g. 'Overall, Isaac will benefit from setting up as a franchise of Petpals™. Even though he may have to give some of his profits to Petpals™, the advantages of operating under the name of an established, trusted company and having support in running his business are likely to mean the business is more successful than it would be if he continued to operate as his own business.'

Page 25 — Business Location

1   B *[1 mark]*

A hairdresser will want to be somewhere that its customers can easily get to. The other companies sell over the internet or phone, or deliver nationally, so being near their customers will be less important.

2   Hint: for the reason you choose, make sure you explain why it would harm the business.

E.g. locating near businesses of the same type means the business will be in direct competition with its neighbours *[1 mark]*, so customers may choose to shop at the competitor businesses *[1 mark]* causing the business to lose sales *[1 mark]*.

3 a)   E.g. DP Oak Ltd. don't rely on people visiting their location for trade *[1 mark]*, as they sell most of their goods over the internet *[1 mark]*.

b)   How to grade your answer:

Level 0: Nothing worthy of credit. *[No marks]*

Level 1: Some attempt has been made to recommend what DP Oak Ltd. should do, but with little justification for why this is the best option. *[1 to 3 marks]*

Level 2: Some of the advantages and disadvantages of each option have been described, along with a justification of which option DP Oak Ltd. should choose. There is some reasoning to the recommendation, but it is lacking in detail or not fully justified. *[4 to 6 marks]*

Level 3: There is a detailed explanation of the advantages and disadvantages of each option, with a well-reasoned and fully justified recommendation of what DP Oak Ltd. should do. *[7 to 9 marks]*

Answers

Here are some points your answer may include:

Option 1

Site 1 is located near a college, which could be convenient for staff if they need training in the skills needed to make the wardrobes.

Site 1 is also on a bus route, so it might be easier to recruit people as they'll be able to get to work more easily.

Site 1 is near an area of high unemployment, so DP Oak Ltd. should be able to find enough people to staff the new factory.

All of these points mean that DP Oak Ltd. might be able to save on recruitment costs and so increase its profits. Being near an area of high unemployment may also mean DP Oak Ltd. can offer lower wages to its staff, so will have lower costs that way too.

However, the company may have to spend more on transporting materials compared to site 2, since site 1 is further away from a wood processing plant.

Option 2

Site 2 is close to a wood processing plant, so transport costs associated with obtaining the raw materials needed to make the wardrobes are likely to be lower. If all other costs remain the same, this should reduce the overall costs/increase the profits of the business.

Site 2 is closer to other, similar, businesses, so it might be easier to find people who already have the skills needed to make the wardrobes.

However, it may be more difficult to find enough staff for the new factory at site 2. This is because site 2 is nearer to an area of high employment and therefore there may not be enough people looking for work nearby. It is also much further away from Hampton than site 1, which has high unemployment, so unemployed people from Hampton are less likely to travel to work there than they would to site 1.

You need to finish your answer with a conclusion recommending which site you think would be best for the new factory — make sure you've looked thoroughly at all the information given. E.g. 'Site 2 would be the best option. Even though it may not be as easy to hire employees at this site, the benefits of cheaper transport costs and the possibility of finding employees who already have the right skills are likely to outweigh this in the long term.'

Pages 26-27— The Marketing Mix

Warm-Up

The different elements of the marketing mix include product, price, promotion and **place**. The product being sold should be something that customers **want** and the price must be **good value**. Promoting a product includes **advertising** it.

1 a) Selling products through the internet *[1 mark]*.

b) Hint: you get one mark for picking out one part of the marketing mix which has been prioritised. Then the second mark is for describing how it has been prioritised.
Ananda has prioritised product *[1 mark]* since WorkOut Ltd. sells high quality products *[1 mark]*. / Ananda has prioritised place *[1 mark]*, since WorkOut Ltd. sells its products in places that are convenient to his customers *[1 mark]*.

c) E.g. by regularly assessing customer needs, Ananda will know when customer needs change *[1 mark]*, and therefore will be able to adapt his marketing mix to meet these new needs *[1 mark]*.

2 E.g. small businesses can't benefit from economies of scale like large businesses can *[1 mark]*, because they can't buy raw materials in large enough quantities / they may not have the equipment to make their processes as efficient as possible *[1 mark]*, so they will have to sell their products at higher prices in order to make enough profit *[1 mark]*.

3 E.g. the product range is likely to be smaller *[1 mark]*, because a smaller business is likely to have less money *[1 mark]* and therefore wouldn't be able to afford to develop lots of different products *[1 mark]*.

4 a) E.g. Williamson's sells kitchenware items which are essential *[1 mark]*, and are therefore likely to meet their customers' needs / so their customers are likely to want to buy them *[1 mark]*. / Williamson's sells high quality items *[1 mark]*, so customers are likely to be satisfied with their purchases *[1 mark]*.

b) How to grade your answer:
Level 0: Nothing worthy of credit. *[No marks]*
Level 1: There is some attempt to describe the impact that the opening of DiscountDishes could have on Williamson's marketing mix, but with little explanation of how DiscountDishes may cause this impact. *[1 to 2 marks]*
Level 2: There is a good description of the impact that the opening of DiscountDishes could have on Williamson's marketing mix, with some explanation of how DiscountDishes may have caused this impact. *[3 to 4 marks]*
Level 3: There is a detailed description of the impact that the opening of DiscountDishes could have on Williamson's marketing mix, and a clear explanation of how DiscountDishes may have caused this impact. *[5 to 6 marks]*

Here are some points your answer may include:
DiscountDishes sells similar items at a cheaper price than Williamson's. Therefore it may take some customers from Williamson's. Currently, Williamson's sells all its products with a 15% profit margin (it uses a cost-plus pricing strategy).

Williamson's may have to lower its prices (e.g. use a competitive pricing strategy) and charge similar prices to DiscountDishes in order to avoid losing customers. However, Williamson's products are a higher quality, so customers may be happy to pay the higher price.

Williamson's doesn't currently have very effective promotion, as most of the customers have heard about the shop from friends, rather than from promotional material. DiscountDishes have put up posters in the shopping centre, so any customers in the shopping centre who are looking to find kitchenware may be more likely to go to DiscountDishes than Williamson's, as they will know they are there. DiscountDishes are also offering a free gift to customers who spend more than £15, which may persuade customers to go there, rather than Williamson's. Therefore Williamson's may decide to increase the amount it spends on promoting its store, in order to make more customers aware that it is there. Williamson's may also decide to emphasise the high quality of its products in its promotional material in order to attract more customers and differentiate itself from DiscountDishes.

Williamson's may decide to ensure that their product range is larger than DiscountDishes' to make the store more competitive.

Page 28 — Business Plans

1   C *[1 mark]* and E *[1 mark]*

2 a)   Sam could have used market research *[1 mark]*.

  b)   E.g. Sam should include the amount of money he needs to start the business *[1 mark]* so he can find appropriate sources of finance *[1 mark]*.

3   How to grade your answer:

   Level 0: Nothing worthy of credit. *[No marks]*

   Level 1: There is some attempt to describe the benefits of having a business plan, but with little discussion of what these benefits mean for the business. *[1 to 2 marks]*

   Level 2: There is a description of a number of different benefits of writing a business plan, with some discussion of what these benefits mean for the business. *[3 to 4 marks]*

   Level 3: There is a detailed description of the different benefits of writing a business plan, and a clear discussion of what these benefits mean for the business. *[5 to 6 marks]*

   Here are some points your answer may include:

   Business plans can help the owner to make business decisions.

   This means that the owner can make decisions that are most likely to benefit the business, which will help it to grow and achieve its aims.

   Business plans can help convince a financial backer that a business idea is a sound investment.

   This means it may be easier to raise the funds to start the business.

   Business plans can show whether a business idea is likely to fail.

   This means the owner can choose not to continue with the idea early, before they have wasted too much time or money.

Page 29 — Stakeholders

1 a)   E.g. customers will want lower prices *[1 mark]*, and Heyshore Sports Ltd. have satisfied this objective by lowering their membership fees by 3% *[1 mark]*.

  b)   Hint: to answer this question, you need to consider how the government could benefit from the business's current activities.

   E.g. one way the government raises money is by taxing the profits that businesses make *[1 mark]* and Heyshore Sports Ltd.'s business activities have resulted in a 20% increase in profits over the last five years *[1 mark]*.

  c)   E.g. the owners will want the business to make as much profit as possible *[1 mark]* and increasing staff wages will increase Heyshore Sports Ltd.'s costs, meaning they may make less profit *[1 mark]*.

  d)   How to grade your answer:

   Level 0: Nothing worthy of credit. *[No marks]*

   Level 1: Some attempt has been made to recommend which option Heyshore Sports Ltd. should choose, but with little justification for why this is the better option. *[1 to 3 marks]*

   Level 2: Some of the advantages and disadvantages to stakeholders of each option have been given, along with a recommendation of which option Heyshore Sports Ltd. should choose. There is some reasoning to the recommendation, but it is lacking in detail or not fully justified.

[4 to 6 marks]

   Level 3: There is a detailed explanation of the advantages and disadvantages to stakeholders of each option, with a well-reasoned and fully justified recommendation of what Heyshore Sports Ltd. should do. *[7 to 9 marks]*

   Here are some points your answer may include:

   Option 1

   The site is directly behind the sports centre, meaning it will be easy for the sports centre's customers to get to. This may increase customer satisfaction and help to attract new customers. Having all the facilities on one site may also make life easier for the employees and managers, so they will be happy.

   The building work at the site is expected to be cheaper than the second option. Lower costs may mean that the expansion is more profitable. The potential to be more profitable is likely to please the business owners, as it may mean they get higher dividends. It is also likely to please employees and managers as it offers them greater job security and may lead to further pay rises for them.

   However, Option 1 uses land which is currently a popular picnic spot. The local community may be unhappy with Heyshore Sports Ltd. if they use the land for sports facilities. Also, the local environmental group will be unhappy with Heyshore Sports Ltd. because using the meadowland would probably have a negative impact on the wildlife in the area. The environmental group may persuade other members of the community that Heyshore Sports Ltd. has made a bad decision, which may result in a loss of custom and revenue for the firm, which could lead to lower profits.

   Option 2

   The site is currently occupied by a derelict factory. Clearing the old factory and using the land for sports facilities might please the local community as it will be more visually appealing.

   Using this site might also please the local environmental group as its unlikely to cause as much harm to the wildlife in the area as using the area of meadowland would.

   The site is twice the size of the first option, meaning it may be able to have more facilities and attract more customers. This could increase the revenue it generates, which may lead to higher profits. Higher profits are likely to lead to higher dividends for the owners, and greater job security and possible pay rises for employees and managers.

   However, building work at the site is likely to be more expensive than on the meadowland. Heyshore Sports Ltd. may need to increase its membership fees to cover these greater costs, meaning customers may be unhappy. It may also need to use more profit to fund the expansion, meaning the owners will be unhappy as they may receive lower dividends.

   The new facilities would be further away from the current sports centre than if Heyshore Sports Ltd. used the meadowland. This may mean that customers would be less willing to use the new facilities, and so Heyshore Sports Ltd. may not see a big increase in revenue as a result of the new facilities.

You need to finish your answer with a conclusion recommending which option you think would be better — make sure you've looked thoroughly at all the information given. E.g. 'Heyshore Sports Ltd. should build their new sports facilities on the meadowland behind the sports centre. Having all the sports facilities near to each other is likely to be more convenient for customers, which may increase customer satisfaction and may help to attract new customers when the new facilities are built, both of which could lead to increased profit for the business. Increased profits would please lots of Heyshore Sports Ltd.'s stakeholders, including the business owners, employees and managers.'

Pages 30-31 — Technology and Business

1   A *[1 mark]*, D *[1 mark]*
2 a)   Jun-Aug *[1 mark]*
Having an e-commerce website developed is likely to have cost a lot of money, so you need to look for the 3-month period in which her costs were highest.

   b)   E.g. the e-commerce website will give Luanne a larger market to sell her products to *[1 mark]*, so she is likely to see her sales continue to increase *[1 mark]*.

   c)   E.g. PayPal will mean that customers find it easier/ faster/safer to buy products from Luanne's website *[1 mark]*, so they will be more likely to complete their online purchases which will lead to increased sales *[1 mark]*.

3 a)   E.g. social media / websites / email *[1 mark]*

   b)   Hint: you should choose one of the 'four Ps' of the marketing mix (product, price, promotion or place) and describe how the mobile app could affect it.
E.g. the app would change the way that Special Pets and More promotes itself *[1 mark]*, as the app would be used to advertise the pets it has available for re-homing *[1 mark]*.

   c)   How to grade your answer:
Level 0: Nothing worthy of credit. *[No marks]*
Level 1: There is some attempt to describe the impact that having a mobile app developed could have on Special Pets and More, but with little explanation of how this could be an advantage and a disadvantage to the firm. *[1 to 2 marks]*
Level 2: There is a good description of how having a mobile app developed could impact Special Pets and More, with some explanation of how this could be an advantage and a disadvantage to the firm. *[3 to 4 marks]*
Level 3: There is a detailed description of how having a mobile app developed could impact Special Pets and More, and a clear explanation of how this could be an advantage and a disadvantage to the firm. *[5 to 6 marks]*
Here are some points your answer may include:
Knowing more about the animals via the mobile app than they can see from an advert in the shop window could persuade people to visit Special Pets and More's shop to see the animals. This makes it more likely that they will buy the animals, which would increase the firm's revenue. While they are at the shop, customers are also likely to buy other items, which would increase the firm's revenue further. This would help Special Pets and More to recover some of the costs that they have encountered from renting the extra shop and taking on two extra employees.

However, the mobile app is likely to be expensive to develop and maintain, so the firm will need to consider whether it can afford the app on top of the extra costs it has already encountered. Also, Special Pets and More might find it difficult to get enough people to download and use the app for it to positively affect sales.

Page 32 — Employment and the Law
Warm-Up
An accountancy firm only recruits people who are under 50 years old.
A nursery pays female supervisors more than male supervisors.
A sports centre refuses to recruit anyone who needs to use a wheelchair.

1 a)   Any two from: e.g. they may be prosecuted / fined / closed down. / They may have to pay compensation. / They may get bad publicity.
[2 marks — 1 mark for each correct answer.]

   b)   E.g. it could be expensive for Coffee Tonight *[1 mark]*, because they will have to provide safety equipment to staff / training *[1 mark]*.

2 a)   E.g. by having a minimum wage, Entertainment World's staff are more likely to be motivated *[1 mark]* and therefore may be more productive for the business *[1 mark]*.

   b)   E.g. by having to pay their staff a minimum wage, Entertainment World will have increased costs *[1 mark]*, which may mean that their profits are reduced *[1 mark]*.

Page 33 — Consumer Law

1 a)   E.g. if the DVD doesn't play through then it's not of satisfactory quality to meet consumer law *[1 mark]*. / If the DVD doesn't match its case then it's a false trade description and so doesn't meet consumer law *[1 mark]*.

   b)   E.g. money back / a repair / a replacement *[1 mark]*

   c)   E.g. he shouldn't sell any DVDs that do not play properly *[1 mark]*. / For any DVDs that are in the wrong DVD case he should repackage them so that the packaging correctly describes the DVD inside *[1 mark]*.

2   Hint: you need to state one way in which profit might be affected for one mark and then give a full explanation for the other two marks.
E.g. it may have to give a refund, replace or repair the faulty products *[1 mark]*, which will cost the business money *[1 mark]* and is likely to lead to a decrease in profit *[1 mark]*. / It may have to defend itself in court *[1 mark]*, which would cost money *[1 mark]* and is likely to lead to a decrease in profit *[1 mark]*. / The reputation of the business may be damaged *[1 mark]*, which could lead to a drop in sales *[1 mark]* and is likely to lead to a decrease in profit *[1 mark]*.

3   E.g. they may make changes to the terms and conditions they give to their customers / retrain their staff *[1 mark]* so that they continue to operate within the law *[1 mark]*. This means they don't risk falling sales / a damaged reputation / high costs that they could encounter if they break the law *[1 mark]*.

Page 34 — Unemployment and Government Taxes

1   E.g. it may mean that people have less money to spend *[1 mark]*. This could mean that there is less demand for and fewer sales of the products or services offered by the business *[1 mark]*, which could lead to lower profits *[1 mark]*.

2   Hint: don't forget that you have to explain an advantage for a business that is just starting up — don't explain anything that would only apply to a more established business.
E.g. high unemployment may mean that people may be willing to work for the business for lower wages *[1 mark]*. This would reduce the business's costs *[1 mark]*, meaning that it could make more profit *[1 mark]*. / High unemployment may mean that a business can easily recruit people as there are lots of people available for work *[1 mark]*. This could reduce the business's recruitment costs *[1 mark]*, meaning that it could make more profit *[1 mark]*. / During times of high unemployment, the government may give grants to businesses who can provide jobs *[1 mark]*. The business could use the money from the grant to cover some of its start-up costs *[1 mark]*, meaning it could make more profit *[1 mark]*.

3 a) E.g. a fall in income tax will mean that people have more disposable income *[1 mark]*, which means Country Rides' revenue is likely to increase *[1 mark]*.

  b) How to grade your answer:
Level 0: Nothing worthy of credit. *[No marks]*
Level 1: There is some attempt to describe the impact that a rise in taxation would have on Country Rides, but with little explanation of how this could be an advantage and a disadvantage to the firm. *[1 to 2 marks]*
Level 2: There is a good description of how the rise in taxation would impact Country Rides, with some explanation of how this could be an advantage and a disadvantage to the firm. *[3 to 4 marks]*
Level 3: There is a detailed description of how the rise in taxation would impact Country Rides, and a clear explanation of how this could be an advantage and a disadvantage to the firm. *[5 to 6 marks]*
Here are some points your answer may include:
If Country Rides has to pay more in tax it will reduce the amount of money it has available to reinvest. This may mean it cannot afford to buy as much land and as many horses as it would like. This means it would not be able to grow as quickly as it otherwise would and may not be as profitable.
However, a rise in the taxes that small businesses have to pay may deter other people from setting up businesses to compete with Country Rides. This would be an advantage to Country Rides, as it reduces the risk that it will lose revenue to competitors.

Page 35 — Inflation and Consumer Income

1   Hint: to answer this question, first of all think about what is meant by a low inflation rate — it means that the price of goods and services isn't rising very quickly. Then think about how this might affect the demand for UK goods from overseas.
E.g. a low inflation rate in the UK makes exports cheaper *[1 mark]*. This means a UK firm that exports goods may experience increased sales *[1 mark]*, which can lead to higher profits *[1 mark]*.

2 a) 2011 *[1 mark]*
  b) 4.8% *[1 mark]*
  c) E.g. the average weekly income increased by a smaller amount/at a slower rate than inflation between 2006 and 2017 *[1 mark]*. Therefore, a typical consumer won't have as much money available to spend on luxury items *[1 mark]*, so demand for and therefore sales of these items may decrease *[1 mark]*.

Page 36 — Interest Rates

1   B *[1 mark]*
2 a) 1984 *[1 mark]*
  b) 1984 was the year in which interest rates were at their highest *[1 mark]*.
  c) Interest rates decreased overall between 1980 and 2010 *[1 mark]*. When interest rates decrease, borrowing becomes cheaper (and saving money less beneficial) *[1 mark]*, so there would have been increased consumer spending *[1 mark]*.

Page 37 — Exchange Rates

Warm-Up
Imports are goods that are bought from a different country.
Exports are goods that are sold to a different country.
If the value of the British pound decreases, British exports will be **cheaper** abroad.

1   D *[1 mark]*
2 a) The amount of CNY which can be bought using INR for the same price has decreased / INR has become cheaper *[1 mark]*. So it will be cheaper for the Chinese company to import raw materials from India *[1 mark]*. This means that they will be able to make their hats more cheaply *[1 mark]*.
  b) The amount of CNY which can be bought using USD for the same price will have increased / USD has become more expensive *[1 mark]*, which means that the Chinese company's hats will be relatively cheaper to buy in the USA *[1 mark]*. This should result in greater sales of the hats *[1 mark]*.

Pages 38-39 — Business Growth

Warm-Up
merger — When two firms join together to form a new, but larger firm.
takeover — When a firm grows by buying more than half the shares in another firm.

1   E.g. internal growth is slow *[1 mark]* as the business grows by expanding its own activities *[1 mark]*, so it may take a long time for profits and sales to increase *[1 mark]*.

2   Hint: to get both marks here, you need to clearly state a benefit of using a website, and describe how this could affect Purrfect Catz Ltd.
E.g. selling products via the internet means that the business has access to a much larger market *[1 mark]*, so its sales are likely to increase *[1 mark]*.

3 How to grade your answer:

Level 0: Nothing worthy of credit. *[No marks]*

Level 1: There is some attempt to describe the ways that a business can expand using organic growth, but with little discussion of how these methods cause the business to grow. *[1 to 2 marks]*

Level 2: A number of different ways that a business may expand by organic growth have been described, with some discussion of how these methods cause the business to grow. *[3 to 4 marks]*

Level 3: There is a detailed description of the different ways that a business can expand by organic growth, and a clear discussion of how these methods cause the business to grow. *[5 to 6 marks]*

Here are some points your answer may include:
A business could target new markets. This should increase the number of customers who want to buy the product, which will increase sales.
To do this, the business could sell products using e-commerce, which means people who don't live near a store can still buy products. So sales should increase.
Technology can mean that items are cheaper to produce. So this could allow the business to target a lower income market.
The business could also change the marketing mix so that the product appeals to a new market.
A business could develop new products through innovation, and research and development.
By selling a brand new product, the business should gain customers, and their sales should increase.

4 a) E.g. by taking over a supplier, Relish the Day will be able to control the supply/cost/quality of its fruit and vegetables *[1 mark]*, so its costs may go down / quality may go up *[1 mark]*.

b) **£1.12** *[1 mark]*
The average unit cost is the average cost divided by the number of jars produced. So 224 000 ÷ 200 000 = £1.12

c) E.g. the firm will be larger, so will be able to buy supplies in greater quantities *[1 mark]*, so the average unit cost of supplies may go down *[1 mark]*. / The firm may be able to operate more advanced machinery *[1 mark]* which may be cheaper to run than before *[1 mark]*.

d) How to grade your answer:

Level 0: Nothing worthy of credit. *[No marks]*

Level 1: There is some attempt to describe the impact that restructuring the hierarchy of Bailes Farm Ltd. had on Relish the Day, but with little explanation of the advantages and disadvantages to the firm. *[1 to 2 marks]*

Level 2: There is a good description of the impact that restructuring the hierarchy of Bailes Farm Ltd. may have had on Relish the Day, with some explanation of the advantages and disadvantages to the firm. *[3 to 4 marks]*

Level 3: There is a detailed description of the impact that restructuring the hierarchy of Bailes Farm Ltd. may have had on Relish the Day, and a clear explanation of the advantages and disadvantages to the firm. *[5 to 6 marks]*

Here are some points your answer may include:
By making some staff redundant, Relish the Day would have reduced the overall costs of the two companies from before the takeover. This should have increased the profits of Relish the Day.
Staff at Bailes Farming Ltd. may have been demoralised by the redundancies, which may have led to lower productivity.
If the staff at Bailes Farming Ltd. aren't motivated by the style of the managers from Relish the Day, their productivity might go down.
Lower productivity means the average unit costs of Relish the Day might go up, which may have caused profits to decrease.

Page 40 — Sources of Finance — Large Businesses

1 a) Profit that is reinvested into the business *[1 mark]*.

b) total finance used = 2500 + 3500 + 1000 = £7000
% which is share capital = (2500 ÷ 7000) × 100
= **35.7%** (3 s.f.)
[2 marks for correct answer, otherwise 1 mark for correctly calculating total finance]

2 How to grade your answer:

Level 0: Nothing worthy of credit. *[No marks]*

Level 1: There is some attempt to describe how becoming a public limited company will impact Xu's Letters Ltd., but with little explanation of how the advantages and disadvantages to the firm. *[1 to 2 marks]*

Level 2: There is a good description of how becoming a public limited company will impact Xu's Letters Ltd., with some explanation of the advantages and disadvantages to the firm. *[3 to 4 marks]*

Level 3: There is a detailed description of how becoming a public limited company will impact Xu's Letters Ltd., and a clear explanation of the advantages and disadvantages to the firm. *[5 to 6 marks]*

Here are some points your answer may include:
Converting the company to a PLC means that the company will be able to raise much more capital through selling shares on the stock exchange. This could help to fund the growth that the shareholders are planning. Growth may mean that the company makes more profit.
Converting to a PLC would make it possible for somebody to buy enough shares to take over the company, meaning the Xu family could end up losing overall control. If the management were to change, the aims and objectives of the business might also change.
Converting to a PLC would mean Xu's Letters Ltd. had to publish its accounts each year. This could show competitors if the business is struggling, and so could affect their competitive advantage.

Page 41 — Changes in Business Aims and Objectives

1 a) E.g. Black Box Plc's competitor has started to use more up-to-date technology *[1 mark]*, so they have changed their aims to include developing a new games console in order to stay competitive *[1 mark]*.

b) How to grade your answer:

Level 0: Nothing worthy of credit. *[No marks]*

Level 1: The student has stated some of the advantages and disadvantages of the ways that Black Box Plc's aims have changed, but with little explanation of whether the changes are likely to be a success for Black Box Plc. *[1 to 4 marks]*

Level 2: There is a detailed description of the advantages and disadvantages of Black Box Plc changing its aims. There is some attempt to conclude whether the changes to the aims are likely to be a success for Black Box Plc, but with little or no explanation to justify the conclusion. *[5 to 8 marks]*

Level 3: There is a detailed and thorough analysis of the advantages and disadvantages of Black Box Plc changing its aims. A conclusion has been made as to whether the changes to the aims are likely to be a success for Black Box Plc, which has been fully justified using evidence. *[9 to 12 marks]*

Here are some points your answer may include:

A company may change its aims to focus on survival, rather than growth.

Black Box Plc have changed their aim from growing their market share from 21% to maintaining their market share of 18%.

This is because, between 2015 and 2016, Black Box Plc's market share fell by 3% as a result of their competitor releasing a new, more technologically advanced games console.

Changing their aim from increasing market share to maintaining market share is likely to be successful, as it will focus the business on methods it can use to prevent sales of the Gold Chest falling further.

Even though this means sales won't increase, it should prevent Black Box Plc from overspending, and should allow the business to survive.

Similarly, changing their sales aim from 30 million to 28 million units by the end of 2016 should ensure that Black Box Plc don't waste money on producing games consoles that they are unlikely to sell. So their profits shouldn't be affected by wasted costs.

A company may change its aims to entering new markets.

Black Box Plc have decided to enter a new market by reducing the price of the Gold Chest, and targeting a lower income market. This will differentiate the Gold Chest from the competitor product, as people who can't afford the new games console might choose to buy the Gold Chest instead.

So Black Box Plc might be able to maintain their market share, even if their revenue falls due to the lower price.

A company can change its aims by changing the size of its product range.

Black Box Plc have decided to increase the size of their product range by developing a new games console.

This will be very expensive for Black Box Plc, so their profits will be reduced.

However, it's important for Black Box Plc to adapt to changing technology in order to stay competitive.

In the long term, developing a new games console should help Black Box Plc to increase their sales, as the new console will use more up-to-date technology than the Gold Chest, so will be able to compete better with the competitor games console. So it should increase Black Box Plc's sales.

By the time the new games console is launched, technology may have developed further, and virtual reality may not be such a cutting edge idea. So sales demand might not be as high as hoped, and sales might not cover the high costs of development. This could mean that Black Box Plc makes a loss on the new games console.

You need to finish your answer with a conclusion about whether or not the changes in aims will be a success for Black Box Plc — make sure you've looked thoroughly at all the information given. E.g. 'Overall, the changes in aims should be a success for Black Box Plc by helping to control their costs and maintain their sales. However, the aim to develop a new games console using virtual reality technology might be risky if they spend a lot of money developing a console using technology that is out of date by the time it is launched. It might be better to use this money to develop other technology that would be more cutting edge and differentiate it from its competitor, which would help to increase sales again in the future.'

Page 42 — Globalisation

1 E.g. companies may have to pay tariffs to import goods into another country *[1 mark]*. This means the company may have to charge higher prices than its competitors for its goods in those countries *[1 mark]* which could reduce its sales if consumers buy goods from competitors instead *[1 mark]*.

2 a) A single business that operates in more than one country *[1 mark]*.

b) E.g. the factory workers in Spain will be paid less per month than the factory workers in the UK *[1 mark]*, so Squishie's average unit costs will be lower/Squishie's wage bill will be less than if they built the new factory in the UK *[1 mark]*.

3 How to grade your answer:

Level 0: Nothing worthy of credit. *[No marks]*

Level 1: There is some attempt to describe the ways that a business can change their marketing mix, but with little discussion of how these changes could help it to compete internationally. *[1 to 2 marks]*

Level 2: A number of different ways that a business may change its marketing mix have been described, with some discussion of how these changes can help the business to compete internationally. *[3 to 4 marks]*

Level 3: There is a detailed description of the different ways that a business can change its marketing mix, and a clear discussion of how these changes can help the business to compete internationally. *[5 to 6 marks]*

Here are some points your answer may include:

The business could change its prices so that they are similar to competitor prices in each country they are selling in.

This means that the pricing of their products should be competitive and there should be demand for their products, so they should have good sales.

The business could change promotion to target the culture of the country they are selling in.

This should mean the product appeals to people in that

country, so they're more likely to buy it.

The business could change the product design to make it relevant to people in the country they are selling in. This should mean that the product satisfies customer needs, and so there will be demand for it.

The business could sell its products to international markets using e-commerce.

This means they can compete overseas without having to set up stores and infrastructure abroad, which will keep their costs down. This means prices can be low, so sales will be good / the business will make more of a profit.

Page 43 — Ethical Considerations

1   C *[1 mark]*, E *[1 mark]*

2 a)   E.g. ensuring that it rewards its staff fairly. / Ensuring that it keeps personal details of staff private. / Ensuring that it provides a comfortable working environment *[1 mark]*.

    b)   E.g. using non-toxic materials. / Paying close attention to safety. / Not using animal testing *[1 mark]*.

3   How to grade your answer:

Level 0: Nothing worthy of credit. *[No marks]*

Level 1: There is some attempt to describe how using a source of Fair Trade coffee beans will impact Beancraft Ltd., but with little explanation of the advantages and disadvantages to the firm. *[1 to 2 marks]*

Level 2: There is a good description of how using a source of Fair Trade coffee beans will impact Beancraft Ltd., with some explanation of the advantages and disadvantages to the firm. *[3 to 4 marks]*

Level 3: There is a detailed description of how using a source of Fair Trade coffee beans will impact Beancraft Ltd., and a clear explanation of the advantages and disadvantages to the firm. *[5 to 6 marks]*

Here are some points your answer may include:

Workers on coffee bean plantations that are Fair Trade certified will get a fair wage, which will allow them to afford a better quality of life. However, buying only from Fair Trade certified plantations may mean that Beancraft Ltd. will have to pay more for coffee beans than its competitors. This could mean that the prices of its coffee products are higher than those of its competitors. This may mean that consumers choose its competitors' coffee instead of Beancraft Ltd.'s, leading to a loss in revenue.

Beancraft Ltd. will also have a smaller selection of plantations to buy from than its competitors, since a smaller number of plantations are fair trade certified than those that are not. This may mean that it won't be able to offer varieties of coffee that its competitors offer, which may mean that customers won't choose its products and it will have a loss in revenue.

However, Beancraft Ltd. may be able to include details of its use of Fair Trade sources of coffee beans in its marketing, in order to emphasise the company's ethical principles. Most of its competitors do not use fair trade sources of coffee beans, so emphasising the use of fair trade sources in Beancraft Ltd.'s marketing could help it to stand out from its competition. This

may mean that customers who want to buy ethical products will choose Beancraft Ltd.'s coffee over its competitors'. This will lead to an increase in revenue for Beancraft Ltd.

Page 44 — Environmental Influences

1   E.g. customers might start to view the business in a negative way *[1 mark]*, so might stop buying products from them *[1 mark]*. This will reduce the business's sales revenue *[1 mark]*.

2 a)   E.g. they could reduce the amount of packaging on products *[1 mark]*, so that less waste goes to landfill *[1 mark]*. / They could use machinery which is quieter *[1 mark]* to reduce noise pollution *[1 mark]*.

    b)   E.g. it could improve the image of ForKids *[1 mark]* which will attract new customers / increase sales *[1 mark]*.

    c)   E.g. it may be expensive *[1 mark]* because new equipment / new processes will be needed *[1 mark]*.

Page 45 — The Marketing Mix and the Design Mix

Warm-Up

You should have circled: how functional the product is, the aesthetics of the product and the cost of making the product.

1   B *[1 mark]*

2 a)   Hint: the method of distribution is how the product gets to customers — in this case, through high street retailers. You should give one way in which the product may be promoted in a high street shop for one mark, and a description of why this method may be used for a second mark.

E.g. SwimTech may use posters in the shops that sell the watch *[1 mark]*, as customers in the shops will see them and may be persuaded to buy a watch *[1 mark]*.

    b)   E.g. differentiating the product will mean that the customers may choose this product over competitors' products *[1 mark]*, which will increase sales for SwimTech *[1 mark]*.

Page 46 — Product Life Cycles

1   B *[1 mark]*

2   E.g. The business's revenue will decrease *[1 mark]* because rival products will begin to take over in the market *[1 mark]* and therefore demand for the product will decrease *[1 mark]*.

3 a)   C *[1 mark]*

    b)   Research will have been carried out *[1 mark]* and the idea for the weedkiller would then have been developed to create a marketable product *[1 mark]*.

Page 47 — Extension Strategies

1   C *[1 mark]*

2   A product in the decline phase of its life cycle will have decreasing sales *[1 mark]*. Lowering the price may mean that more customers will be willing to buy the product *[1 mark]*, which will extend the life of the product *[1 mark]*.

3   How to grade your answer:
     Level 0: Nothing worthy of credit. *[No marks]*
     Level 1: Some of the advantages and disadvantages
              of the extension strategies Nestlé® have used
              have been given, but with little explanation
              of whether the extension strategies are
              likely to have been beneficial for Nestlé®.
              [1 to 4 marks]
     Level 2: There is a detailed description of the
              advantages and disadvantages of Nestlé®
              using extension strategies. There is some
              attempt to conclude whether the extension
              strategies are likely to have been beneficial
              for Nestlé®, but with little or no explanation to
              justify the conclusion. *[5 to 8 marks]*
     Level 3: There is a detailed and thorough analysis
              of the advantages and disadvantages of the
              extension strategies Nestlé® have used. A
              conclusion has been made as to whether the
              extension strategies are likely to have been
              beneficial for Nestlé®, which has been fully
              justified using evidence. *[9 to 12 marks]*

Here are some points your answer may include:
A company can extend the life of a product by adding
more features.
A company can also extend the life of a product by
targeting a different market.
Nestlé® originally extended the life of its KitKat® range
by developing new products in the range, such as the
KitKat® Chunky and new flavours of KitKat®. These
new products may have appealed to a different target
market interested in different forms of chocolate bar,
so would have increased demand for KitKat®.
Although Nestlé® would have increased their costs by
developing the new products, they will have benefited
from the increased sales revenue, and from maintaining
KitKat® as one of the most popular brands in the UK.
However, the extension strategy was not enough to
ensure KitKat®'s continued success, as in 2014 KitKat®
sales and market share decreased.
Nestlé® could have used the money spent on the
extension strategy to develop and launch a completely
new product. However, it would have taken a long
time to establish a new product to have a market share
similar to KitKat®'s. The increase in revenue from
KitKat® before 2014 is likely to have been greater than
the revenue that would have been generated from a
completely new product in the same time.
A company can extend the life of a product by updating
packaging. In 2015, Nestlé® changed the packaging
of KitKat®. This is likely to have made KitKat®s more
eye-catching to consumers. They also added a feature
to the packaging that included a link to an online video.
This may have meant customers were more interested
in buying the chocolate in order to watch the video.
Both of these strategies may have increased demand for
the KitKat®. The extension strategies were expensive,
costing £10m. This would have increased Nestlé®'s
costs. However, the campaign should have increased
the revenue of KitKat® by increasing demand, which
should have covered these costs.

This may have meant that Nestlé® will have reduced
costs overall, as instead of spending money developing
and promoting a new product, it has been able to
extend the life of one of its current products.
*You need to finish your answer with a conclusion about whether or not the
extension strategies would have benefitted Nestlé® overall — make sure
you've looked thoroughly at all the information given. E.g. 'As KitKat®
is one of the most popular chocolate bars in the UK, it is likely to be an
important source of revenue for Nestlé®. Despite the costs associated
with the extension strategies, the increase in revenue they cause should be
enough to cover these costs. So using extension strategies should ultimately
have increased profits and so benefitted Nestlé®.'*

Page 48 — Price

1   E.g. a product may be priced similarly to competitors'
     products within the market *[1 mark]*, as if the price is
     too high then customers' may choose a competitor's
     product *[1 mark]*, so the company's revenue will be
     lower *[1 mark]*.
*There are a couple of explanations you could have given to explain why
prices may be similar to competitors' prices — if the price is too high,
customers may choose the cheaper products, but if the price is too low, they
might assume the quality is lower. Both these factors could decrease sales.*

2   E.g. using technology can make producing products
     more efficient *[1 mark]*, which lowers the cost of
     making them *[1 mark]*. So a business can charge lower
     prices whilst still making a profit *[1 mark]*.

3 a) E.g. the Indigo Night collection is in the decline
     phase, so demand is falling *[1 mark]*. Decreasing the
     price should increase demand for the collection again
     [1 mark].

  b) E.g. the Crystal Gold collection is of a higher quality
     than the other collections / is being targeted at a
     different market segment *[1 mark]*. So customers
     may be more willing to pay more for the collection
     [1 mark].

Page 49 — Pricing Strategies

Warm-Up
true, false, true

1 a) Amount added to price = 4.40 × 0.7 = 3.08
     Price = 4.40 + 3.08 = **£7.48**
     *[2 marks for correct answer, otherwise 1 mark for
     using the correct calculation.]*

  b) How to grade your answer:
     Level 0: Nothing worthy of credit. *[No marks]*
     Level 1: Some attempt is made to recommend what
              pricing strategy ElectricPages Ltd. should use,
              but with little justification for why this should
              be done. *[1 to 3 marks]*
     Level 2: Some of the advantages and disadvantages of
              both strategies have been given, along with a
              recommendation for which one ElectricPages
              Ltd. should use. There is some reasoning to
              the recommendation, but it is lacking in detail
              or not fully justified. *[4 to 6 marks]*
     Level 3: There is a thorough description of the
              advantages and disadvantages of both
              strategies, with a well-reasoned and fully
              justified recommendation of which strategy
              ElectricPages Ltd. should use. *[7 to 9 marks]*

Here are some points your answer may include:

<u>Setting the price below cost:</u>

This strategy would generate a loss per product sold. Therefore this strategy would be very costly for ElectricPages Ltd.

This strategy may be risky as if their sales of other products aren't high enough, they may not be able to cover the cost of selling the EezyReadr at a loss.

However using this strategy may mean that the e-reader will be cheaper than other e-readers on the market, which will encourage people to buy it. This will help to establish a market share.

The fact that e-books from other companies are not compatible with the device may mean that fewer customers would be willing to buy the device, so charging a low cost may help to persuade customers that it is worth buying.

E-books are much cheaper to make than e-readers and the company keeps a large percentage of the sales of e-books as profit.

By pricing the e-reader below the cost of making it, the company will encourage customers to buy their e-books, since only e-books bought from ElectricPages Ltd.'s website are compatible with the device.

Therefore, even though they will make a loss on the EezyReadr using this strategy, they could still earn profit through sales of e-books from their website.

<u>Charging a high price when it is released:</u>

This would be beneficial for ElectricPages Ltd. since they would be able to cover the costs of the research and development of the EezyReadr and may make a profit.

Charging a high price at first may be suitable for the EezyReadr because it may have a high demand when it is first introduced due to its new technological features.

However, a high price may mean that the product will not appeal to the mass market and so this will reduce sales of the product.

Although it has new features, it is not the first e-reader on the market, so it might not benefit very much from this strategy as there might not be enough demand for the EezyReadr.

Charging a high price for the EezyReadr may give it a good image and may make it more appealing to people with high incomes. This may help to improve ElectricPages Ltd.'s image and status.

You need to finish your answer with a conclusion recommending what you think ElectricPages Ltd. should do — make sure you've looked thoroughly at all the information given. E.g. 'ElectricPages Ltd. should set the price of the Eezyreadr below the cost of making it. Although they will earn less profit per e-reader sold, they are likely to attract more customers and make more profit through sales of e-books and other products.'

Pages 50-51 — *Methods of Promotion*

Warm-Up

An advert in a prime time TV show — A mass market

An advert in a local newspaper — A market in a particular location

An advert in a magazine for teenagers — A market of a particular age

1 E.g. it's important so that the company's overall brand image remains strong *[1 mark]*, since this will mean that all of the company's products will be more easily recognised *[1 mark]* and will be more likely to be bought by customers *[1 mark]*.

2 a) Sponsorship means that the business will give money towards the event *[1 mark]* and in exchange the name of the business is displayed at the event *[1 mark]*.

b) By sponsoring the marathon, Mamo Ltd. will be more likely to be promoted to its target market than sponsoring another kind of event *[1 mark]*, since individuals at the marathon are likely to be interested in sports *[1 mark]*.

3 How to grade your answer:

Level 0: Nothing worthy of credit. *[No marks]*

Level 1: There is some attempt to describe how a business may use technology to promote its products, but with little discussion of how technology can be used to promote to specific market segments. *[1 to 2 marks]*

Level 2: A number of different ways that a business may use technology to promote its products have been described, with some discussion of how technology can be used to promote to specific market segments. *[3 to 4 marks]*

Level 3: There is a detailed description of the ways that a business may use technology to promote its products, and a clear discussion of how technology can be used to promote to specific market segments. *[5 to 6 marks]*

Here are some points your answer may include:

A business may create a social media account to improve its brand image and to advertise its products. Social media accounts may be tailored to be appealing to different market segments, and individual accounts may also be created for separate products in order to target a specific market segment for each product.

Technology can be used to track an individual's internet search history. Businesses can therefore target adverts to people who seem to fit within a particular market segment based on the web pages they have visited in the past.

Technology can be used to track an individual's geographic location. Businesses can use this information to target their advertising to people that are in a particular area.

A business may be able to get individuals from its target market (e.g. previous customers) to sign up to an e-newsletter. In this way, the business can send promotional material directly to its target market using e-mail.

4 How to grade your answer:

Level 0: Nothing worthy of credit. *[No marks]*

Level 1: There is some attempt to describe the impact of using a special offer on Beth's Kitchen, but with little explanation of the advantages and disadvantages to the firm. *[1 to 2 marks]*

Level 2: There is a good description of the impact of using a special offer on Beth's Kitchen with some explanation of the advantages and disadvantages to the firm. *[3 to 4 marks]*

Level 3: There is a detailed description of the impact on Beth's Kitchen of using a special offer, and a clear explanation of the advantages and disadvantages to the firm. *[5 to 6 marks]*

Here are some points your answer may include:

Bethany and her team offered a discount to people who booked with the company while at the wedding show. This may have increased the number of bookings that Beth's Kitchen made while at the wedding show and therefore may have increased revenue for the business. However, since they are discounted, the business will earn less per booking and therefore will not make as much profit for these bookings.

The special offer also may have made Beth's Kitchen look like less of a luxury brand and so may not have attracted customers from market segments interested in luxury.

The special offer may have meant that customers would not be willing to pay the normal price for the business's services and so may mean that Beth's Kitchen will lose out on potential future sales.

Page 52 — Place

1   D *[1 mark]*

2 a)   A business that sells products to customers *[1 mark]*.

b)   E.g. high-street retailers are likely to have employees on hand who can provide better customer service to customers *[1 mark]*, which may help to increase sales of the products *[1 mark]*.

c)   E.g. the online retailers will have lower costs because they won't have to pay to have stores open *[1 mark]* this will mean that the online companies can charge less per product and still make the same amount of profit as the high-street retailers *[1 mark]*.

d)   E.g. Lisa may have many more potential customers by selling through the online companies *[1 mark]*, since these companies may be able to sell to a global market *[1 mark]*.

Pages 53-54 — Methods of Production

Warm-Up

Job production	Flow production
personalised birthday cakes designer clothes tailored suits	pencils chocolate bars cars

1   A *[1 mark]*

2   B *[1 mark]*, D *[1 mark]*

3   E.g. batch production is faster than job production *[1 mark]*, since it involves making batches of identical products at the same time *[1 mark]*, so the firm will be more productive *[1 mark]*.

4 a)   Hint: there's one mark for stating an advantage of job production, and one mark for explaining its impact on the company.
E.g. the sofas made using job production can be made exactly to a customer's specification *[1 mark]*, which could lead to better customer satisfaction *[1 mark]*.

b)   Hint: there's one mark for stating a disadvantage of job production, and one mark for explaining its impact on the company.
E.g. making the sofas using job production is expensive, so could lead to high prices *[1 mark]*, which could mean fewer customers buy sofas from the company, and their sales would be low *[1 mark]*.

c)   How to grade your answer:
Level 0: Nothing written worthy of credit. *[No marks]*
Level 1: There is some attempt to describe how using the new technology will impact Sofa-So-Good Ltd., but with little explanation of the advantages and disadvantages to the firm. *[1 to 2 marks]*
Level 2: There is a good description of how using the new technology will impact Sofa-So-Good Ltd., with some explanation of the advantages and disadvantages to the firm. *[3 to 4 marks]*
Level 3: There is a detailed description of how using the new technology will impact Sofa-So-Good Ltd., and a clear explanation of the advantages and disadvantages to the firm. *[5 to 6 marks]*

Here are some points your answer may include:

It is faster to use the machinery to make sofas than to make them by hand, so Sofa-So-Good Ltd.'s productivity will increase. This may increase their sales as they'll be able to produce more sofas in a set period of time, and customers won't have to wait as long for their sofa to be completed.

The machinery has reduced the amount of waste Sofa-So-Good Ltd. produce, which should reduce their costs as they won't need to buy as large quantities of raw materials.

The machinery can be operated by workers who are less highly trained than the workers who make the sofas by hand. This means that Sofa-So-Good Ltd. can employ fewer skilled workers. This will decrease the cost of their wage bill.

The machinery is very accurate, so might improve the quality of the sofas made by Sofa-So-Good Ltd. This could help them to compete in the sofa market, and help to increase sales.

Sofa-So-Good Ltd. will have to train staff to use the new machinery, which could be expensive, and so will increase their costs until training is finished.

The new machinery cost £20 000, so if Sofa-So-Good Ltd.'s sales don't increase, they could end up making a loss.

It may be expensive to maintain the machinery, which may increase Sofa-So-Good Ltd.'s costs.

Using the machinery means that Sofa-So-Good Ltd. is less flexible in the range of sofas that they can offer. This may reduce customer satisfaction, and so reduce their sales.

Page 55 — Managing Stock

1 a)   28 bottles *[1 mark]*
  b)   E.g. floor cleaner is ordered on day 3 and arrives on day 7.
       So time to deliver = 7 − 3 = 4 days
       [2 marks for correct answer, otherwise 1 mark for identifying when orders were made and delivered]

2   How to grade your answer:
     Level 0: Nothing worthy of credit. *[No marks]*
     Level 1: There is some attempt to describe how using just-in-time (JIT) will impact The Reading Shelf, but with little explanation of the advantages and disadvantages to the firm. *[1 to 2 marks]*
     Level 2: There is a good description of how using JIT will impact The Reading Shelf, with some explanation of the advantages and disadvantages to the firm. *[3 to 4 marks]*
     Level 3: There is a detailed description of how using JIT will impact The Reading Shelf, and a clear explanation of the advantages and disadvantages to the firm. *[5 to 6 marks]*

Here are some points your answer may include:
Switching to JIT means The Reading Shelf will no longer order books in bulk, and will only order the stock they need. It is therefore less likely to make orders over 2000 units and so will not benefit from the discount offered by the supplier on these large orders. Therefore, the costs of their supplies could increase.
However, it means The Reading Shelf won't have as much waste from discarding books that are no longer selling. This could mean their costs go down as they are only spending money on books they know they should sell.
Using JIT means The Reading Shelf will have more frequent deliveries. This means their costs will go up, as they'll have to pay a delivery charge each time. However, The Reading Shelf will no longer need to rent such a large warehouse to store its books, so costs could go down.
Deliveries from the supplier can occasionally be delayed. By changing to just-in-time stock control, The Reading Shelf will not have stock available when deliveries are delayed and will be unable to fulfill orders to bookshops. This may mean that The Reading Shelf will get a bad reputation. This could reduce The Reading Shelf's revenue.

Page 56 — Working with Suppliers

1   B *[1 mark]*
2 a)   E.g. having well managed logistics should improve customer satisfaction *[1 mark]* as the milkshakes should be high quality/a reasonable price *[1 mark]*.
  b)   How to grade your answer:
       Level 0: Nothing worthy of credit. *[No marks]*
       Level 1: Some attempt has been made to recommend which option Shake it Up should take, but with little justification for why this should be done. *[1 to 3 marks]*

     Level 2: Some of the advantages and disadvantages of each option have been given, along with a recommendation of which option Shake it Up should take. There is some reasoning to the recommendation, but it is lacking in detail or not fully justified. *[4 to 6 marks]*
     Level 3: There is a thorough description of the advantages and disadvantages of each option, with a detailed recommendation of which option Shake it Up should take that has been fully justified. *[7 to 9 marks]*

Here are some points your answer may include:
Using the local farm
Buying cream from the farm means that Shake it Up can change their order up to 6pm the day before they collect it. Shake it Up are unsure what the demand for ice cream will be, so being able to change their order at short notice and collect the cream every day should mean they are more likely to order the correct amount. This will cut down on waste, so reduce the business's costs.
The farm has had reliable availability in the past, since it ensures that milk is ready for collection the morning after an order has been placed. Therefore Shake it Up can trust that the farm is likely to be reliable in supplying cream as well.
Shake it Up know that the quality of produce from the farm is good, so buying from the farm should help to ensure the quality of the ice cream is the same standard as the milkshakes.
The farm offers Shake it Up a discount on orders over £4000. If they are ordering cream as well as milk from the farm, they are more likely to be buying this amount, so will benefit from reducing their costs by using the discount.
Shake it Up would have to collect the cream from the farm. They are already paying for someone to collect milk each day, but they may have to invest in a larger van if they are ordering more produce.
Using Ribblethwaites
The cream at Ribblethwaites is cheaper than from the farm, so Shake it Up's costs would be reduced. Ribblethwaites will deliver the cream to Shake it Up, which will mean they don't have to pay for someone to collect the cream.
Shake it Up haven't used Ribblethwaites before, so don't know what the quality of the produce will be. Ribblethwaites may also be unreliable.
Shake it Up would have to order cream a week in advance, which could lead to waste if they order too much, and so increase their costs. If they order too little, they might not be able to complete orders, which could reduce customer satisfaction.
You need to finish your answer with a conclusion recommending what you think Shake it Up should do — make sure you've looked thoroughly at all the information given. E.g. 'Shake it Up should buy cream from the farm. Even though it will be more expensive, this cost difference will be less if they are able to use their discount. The flexibility of being able to change the order up to 6pm the day before is a big advantage, as is the fact they know that the farm has reliable availability and supplies high quality produce.'

Page 57 — Quality

1 Hint: make sure that your answer definitely relates to quality assurance rather than quality control. Quality assurance stops errors from being made in the first place, whereas quality control is about finding faults that have already occurred.

E.g. the firm should waste less materials making faulty products it can't sell *[1 mark]* as products will be checked at each stage in the production process *[1 mark]* which should prevent errors from being made *[1 mark]*.

2 How to grade your answer:

Level 0: Nothing worthy of credit. *[No marks]*

Level 1: There is some attempt to describe the effect the new employees have had on quality, but with little analysis of how this may impact SB Vans. *[1 to 2 marks]*

Level 2: There is a good explanation of the effect the new employees have had on quality, with some analysis of how this may impact SB Vans. *[3 to 4 marks]*

Level 3: There is a detailed explanation of the effect the new employees have had on quality, and a clear analysis of how this may impact SB Vans. *[5 to 6 marks]*

Here are some points your answer may include:
Since the new employees started, the proportion of deliveries which have been delivered within Saif's target of 48 hours has fallen from 88% (24% + 64%) to 78% (24% + 54%). This may lead to customer complaints, as Saif guarantees delivery within 48 hours.

This could cause SB Vans to develop a poor reputation, so it could lose its competitive advantage.

This could lead to the factories deciding not to use SB Vans as their courier service anymore, which would cause the business's sales to fall.

Customers could also ask for compensation for the late deliveries, which may cause SB Vans' costs to go up, and so cause their profits to decrease.

Pages 58-59 — The Sales Process

Warm-Up
1. Finding customers. 2. Approaching customers. 3. Assessing customer needs. 4. Presenting the product to a customer. 5. Getting the customer to buy the item. 6. Following up with the customer after the sale.

1 A *[1 mark]*, E *[1 mark]*

2 E.g. if customers are satisfied with the level of service they receive from a business, they may be more likely to buy products again from the business in the future / recommend it to friends *[1 mark]*. This will lead to an increase in revenue *[1 mark]*. If this increase outweighs any spending on improving customer service, then profits will rise *[1 mark]*.

3 a) E.g. Bee's Travel employs two employees whose sole job is to answer website enquiries *[1 mark]* / Bee's Travel aims to answer website enquiries within 24 hours *[1 mark]*.

b) Hint: you need to give a brief description of how the training in product knowledge will affect customers or staff for one mark and then the impact that this will have on the business for the second mark.
E.g. it will ensure customer queries are answered quickly/accurately *[1 mark]* which will improve customer satisfaction *[1 mark]*. / Staff may be able to recommend additional products to suit a customer's needs *[1 mark]*, which will increase Bee's Travel's sales *[1 mark]*. / It will make customers will feel confident about buying from Bee's Travel *[1 mark]* which is likely to increase sales *[1 mark]*.

c) E.g. Bee's Travel could explain how it will ensure suitcases don't get damaged in the future *[1 mark]* to reassure the customer that she won't have the same experience if she buys from Bee's Travel again *[1 mark]*.

Pages 60-61 — Business Calculations

1 a) The profit a firm makes when all expenses are taken into account *[1 mark]*.

b) gross profit = revenue – cost of sales
= 400 000 – 150 000 = £250 000
net profit = gross profit – (remaining expenses)
net profit = 250 000 – 200 000 = **£50 000**
[4 marks for correct answer, otherwise 1 mark for using the correct equation for gross profit, 1 mark for calculating the correct gross profit, and 1 mark for using the correct equation for net profit]

2 a) gross profit margin = (gross profit ÷ sales revenue) × 100
= (690 000 ÷ 3 000 000) × 100
= **23%**
[2 marks for correct answer, otherwise 1 mark for using the correct equation]

b) net profit = gross profit – (other operating expenses and interest)
= 690 000 – 510 000 = 180 000
net profit margin = (net profit ÷ sales revenue) × 100
= (180 000 ÷ 3 000 000) × 100 = **6%**
[4 marks for correct answer, otherwise 1 mark for using the correct equation for net profit, 1 mark for correctly calculating net profit and 1 mark for using the correct equation to calculate net profit margin]

c) The business has a relatively low net profit margin compared to its gross profit margin *[1 mark]*. Reducing the amount the business spends on insurance would help to increase its net profit margin *[1 mark]*.

d) A reduction in money spent on insurance would not affect the company's gross profit margin *[1 mark]*, because the gross profit margin only takes into account the cost of making the products / does not take into account operating expenses *[1 mark]*.

3 Even though the cost of each product stays the same, the amount of money being spent on each product by customers will increase *[1 mark]*. Therefore a smaller percentage of the money spent by customers will go towards making the product *[1 mark]*, resulting in a higher gross profit margin *[1 mark]*.

4 a) total profit = 170 000 + 130 000 + 150 000 + 150 000
+ 120 000 − 200 000 = £520 000
average annual profit = 520 000 ÷ 5 = £104 000
average rate of return = (average annual profit ÷
initial investment) × 100
average rate of return = (104 000 ÷ 200 000) × 100
= **52%**
[4 marks for correct answer, otherwise 1 mark for correct total profit, 1 mark for correct average annual profit and 1 mark for using the correct equation to calculate the average rate of return]

b) The average rate of return on the investment is quite large *[1 mark]*. This means Speedy Wheels should quickly see its profits increase as a result of the investment *[1 mark]*.

Page 62 — Business Data and Performance

1 A *[1 mark]*, D *[1 mark]*
2 a) £400 000 *[1 mark]*
b) E.g. profitability ratios from different years / cash flow forecasts from different years / profit/loss in different years *[1 mark]*.
c) E.g. the data will not show the reasons why revenue has changed over time *[1 mark]*, and therefore cannot be used on its own to make business decisions *[1 mark]*. / There may be many reasons for changes in revenue over time which will not be due to business performance *[1 mark]*, such as changes in how well the economy is doing *[1 mark]*.

Pages 63-64 — Internal Organisational Structures

Warm-Up
True, True, False, False
1 D *[1 mark]*
2 Hint: you get one mark for stating a disadvantage of a centralised structure. The additional two marks are for explaining how centralisation causes this disadvantage and the overall effect on the firm.
E.g. having a centralised structure can slow down decision-making / communication of decisions reaching employees *[1 mark]* because all major decisions are made by one person or a few senior managers at the top of the structure *[1 mark]*, meaning the firm reacts slowly to change *[1 mark]*.
3 E.g. each manager will have a narrow span of control *[1 mark]*, so they can monitor the employees they are responsible for more closely *[1 mark]* and so the firm may be more effective *[1 mark]*.
4 a) E.g. Claire Wilkinson is likely to be responsible for the overall strategy of Houghton & Son Ltd.'s sales department in the UK *[1 mark]*.
b) E.g. there is a short chain of command *[1 mark]* / each manager has a wide span of control *[1 mark]*.
c) E.g. as the company grew it would have needed more employees *[1 mark]*, and so more managers to organise and control them *[1 mark]*.
d) How to grade your answer:
Level 0: Nothing worthy of credit. *[No marks]*
Level 1: There is some attempt to describe the impact of decentralisation on Houghton and Son Ltd., but with little explanation of the advantages and disadvantages to the firm. *[1 to 2 marks]*
Level 2: There is a good description of the impact of decentralisation on Houghton and Son Ltd., with some explanation of the advantages and disadvantages to the firm. *[3 to 4 marks]*
Level 3: There is a detailed description of the impact of decentralisation on Houghton and Son Ltd., and a clear explanation of the advantages and disadvantages to the firm. *[5 to 6 marks]*
Here are some points your answer may include:
Decentralising the structure of Houghton and Son Ltd. means that the authority to make decisions will be shared out, e.g. to the managers of each branch. This means that the people making the decisions can use their expert knowledge of their branch, leading to better decisions being made. They also won't have to spend time communicating with people further up the hierarchy for approval on their decisions, so changes can be made more quickly.
Also, as senior managers at the top of the hierarchy won't be responsible for making as many decisions, Houghton & Son Ltd. may not need to have a central office where decisions are made, meaning they could reduce their fixed costs and so increase their overall profit.
However, giving managers in different branches the authority to make decisions may mean that inconsistencies develop between the different branches, which could negatively effect their overall brand image. Also, the people making the decisions might not be able to see the overall needs of the business, leading to poor decisions being made.

Page 65 — Communication

1 E.g. effective communication leads to improved staff motivation *[1 mark]*, as staff will know what is happening in the firm *[1 mark]* and therefore will be more confident that they're doing their job properly *[1 mark]*.
2 a) E.g. the distance between the different manufacturing sites *[1 mark]*.
b) How to grade your answer:
Level 0: Nothing worthy of credit. *[No marks]*
Level 1: There is some attempt to describe the impact of insufficient communication on White Days, but with little explanation of the disadvantages to the business. *[1 to 2 marks]*
Level 2: There is a good description of the impact of insufficient communication on White Days, with some explanation of the disadvantages to the business. *[3 to 4 marks]*
Level 3: There is a detailed description of the impact of insufficient communication on White Days, and a clear explanation of the disadvantages to the business. *[5 to 6 marks]*
Here are some points your answer may include:
There was not enough communication from the German site about the problem with the new screws. This meant that the UK site was not prepared for the problem before they started using the new screws, which led to inefficiency and waste as they tried to fix the problem.

The managers did not pass on the decision to make the holes smaller to the assembly line supervisor, or to the workers fitting the hinges. This led to different parts of the assembly line following different instructions and therefore the waste of time and materials. This would have meant a fall in efficiency and an increase in costs for White Days.

The supervisor and the workers may have felt demotivated because they were not kept informed of issues at the German site or decisions being made by managers in the firm, which meant they couldn't do their job properly. This may cause a problem with White Days retaining their staff.

Page 66 — Ways of Working
1   C *[1 mark]*
2 a)   E.g. they may choose their own working hours to fit around other commitments. *[1 mark]*
   b)   freelance contract *[1 mark]*
   c)   How to grade your answer:
     Level 0: Nothing worthy of credit. *[No marks]*
     Level 1: There is some attempt to describe the impact of technology on ways of working at Greta Designs, but with little explanation of the advantages to the business. *[1 to 2 marks]*
     Level 2: There is a good description of the impact of technology on ways of working at Greta Designs, with some explanation of the advantages to the business. *[3 to 4 marks]*
     Level 3: There is a detailed description of the impact of technology on ways of working at Greta Designs, and a clear explanation of the advantages to the business. *[5 to 6 marks]*
   Here are some points your answer may include:
The graphic designers use computer software to design the initial logos as well as the finalised designs. This will mean that the design will be much more accurate than when sketching the design by hand and makes it easier to make changes to the designs, improving the efficiency of the overall design process.
The fact that the graphic designers can now communicate via the firm's website, email, instant messaging service and video calls means that the firm has become more efficient as the graphic designers don't need to spend time setting up and attending meetings with clients. It also means that the graphic designers can work from anywhere as long as they have access to their computer and the internet, so they no longer need to be based in the company's offices and can work remotely instead.

Page 67 — Recruitment
1   B *[1 mark]* and C *[1 mark]*
2 a)   a CV / an application form *[1 mark]*
   b)   E.g. it is more expensive / it is slower / the candidates won't know as much about the firm / bosses in the firm may not know as much about the candidate *[1 mark]*.
   c)   E.g. the adverts will be seen by more people *[1 mark]* so it's more likely that Jasmine will find a nail technician really suited to the role *[1 mark]*.

/ Recruiting people from outside of the business will mean that people with new ideas are brought in *[1 mark]*, which could improve the quality of the service offered in the beauty salons *[1 mark]*. / Recruiting people from outside of the business will mean that there are no internal vacancies left *[1 mark]*, which would cost Jasmine more time and money to fill *[1 mark]*.
   d)   E.g. a person specification would have given information about the qualities/experience Jasmine wants the new nail technician to have *[1 mark]*. By not providing it Jasmine may waste time considering candidates who do not meet her requirements *[1 mark]*.

Page 68 — Training and Development
Warm-Up
Warehouse staff are sent on a course so they can gain a forklift truck licence.
A bank assistant attends a college course to gain mortgage advisor qualifications.
Care workers are taught sign language by a tutor from the British Deaf Association.
1   Hint: there are lots of possible answers here. For the benefit that you give, make sure you explain why it is beneficial to the business.
   E.g. informal training is cost-effective for the business *[1 mark]* because the employee works and learns at the same time *[1 mark]* and the business doesn't have to pay for training from outside tutors *[1 mark]*.
2 a)   E.g. warehouse staff would need training on how to use the new technology *[1 mark]*.
   b)   E.g. in a performance review the manager will check each employee is meeting targets they have been set *[1 mark]*. He can then identify workers that might need more training or support so that they can become better at their jobs *[1 mark]*.
   c)   Training is likely to make staff feel like they are progressing in the firm / that the firm is interested in how well the staff are doing their jobs *[1 mark]*, which is likely to make the staff feel more motivated and more likely to stay with the firm *[1 mark]*.

Pages 69-70 — Motivation
1   A *[1 mark]*
2 a)   Fringe benefits are any rewards given to workers that are not part of their main income *[1 mark]*.
   b)   E.g. the fringe benefits mean that O_2 employees save money *[1 mark]*, which may make them feel motivated to work for O_2 *[1 mark]*.
3   How to grade your answer:
     Level 0: Nothing worthy of credit. *[No marks]*
     Level 1: There is an attempt to describe some non-financial benefits that a firm could give to its employees, but with little discussion of how these would motivate staff. *[1 to 2 marks]*
     Level 2: A number of different non-financial benefits that a firm could give to its employees have been described, with some discussion of how these would motivate staff. *[3 to 4 marks]*

Level 3: There is a detailed description of the different non-financial benefits that a firm could give to its employees, and a clear discussion of how these would motivate staff.
[5 to 6 marks]
Here are some points your answer may include:
A firm could use job rotation, meaning that its employees are occasionally moved from doing one job to another. This may make them feel motivated as it may stop them from becoming bored.
A firm could use job enrichment, meaning that its employees are given greater responsibility. This can make them feel motivated as it will give them new challenges and prevent them from feeling that once they become good at their job they are just given more of the same work to do.
A firm could give their employees autonomy, meaning that they are given the freedom to make their own decisions. This may make them feel motivated as they may feel trusted and like their contribution is valued.

4 a) salaries / commission *[1 mark]*
b) Being given a higher position in the business *[1 mark]*.
c) Money from commission = (19 000 ÷ 100) × 5 = £950
Total amount paid = £1250 + £950 = **£2200**
[2 marks for correct answer, otherwise 1 mark for calculating the money from commission.]
d) How to grade your answer:
Level 0: Nothing worthy of credit. *[No marks]*
Level 1: Some attempt has been made to recommend what Packman's Glazing should do, but with little justification for why this is the better option. *[1 to 3 marks]*
Level 2: Some of the advantages and disadvantages of the two pay schemes have been described, along with a recommendation of which one Packman's Glazing should use. There is some reasoning to the recommendation, but it is lacking in detail or not fully justified.
[4 to 6 marks]
Level 3: There is a detailed explanation of the advantages and disadvantages of the two pay schemes, with a well-reasoned and fully justified recommendation of which one Packman's Glazing should use.
[7 to 9 marks]
Here are some points your answer may include:
Paying sales staff commission will make them more motivated to sell, since the more they sell the more they earn. This will lead to higher productivity in the business.
Having motivated staff can also increase staff retention as workers are less likely to want to leave the business. This can reduce recruitment and training costs for the business.
Having motivated staff may also help to attract new employees to the firm, which will make recruiting new staff easier as there are likely to be lots of applicants for vacancies.
However, two of the sales staff have chosen to leave the business, partly because they would prefer to be paid a higher salary but with no commission.

Workers may prefer this pay scheme as it means they get a higher guaranteed income and they don't have the stress of having to sell lots of products in order to increase their income.
But this scheme may mean that productivity falls as the workers are less motivated to perform well. So moving to this pay scheme could mean that Packman's Glazing's profits would fall, as they would be paying their workers more but may experience falling sales.
As the rival firm is new, it may be too early to tell whether their pay scheme is effective at keeping workers motivated enough to stay with the firm long-term and to sell enough products.
You need to finish your answer with a conclusion recommending what you think Packman's Glazing should do — make sure you've looked thoroughly at all the information given. E.g. 'Packman's Glazing should continue with their current pay scheme. Even though this means that they risk losing staff, their workers are likely to be more motivated to perform well, which could lead to more sales and higher profits for the business.'

Pages 71-77 — Mixed Questions

1 D *[1 mark]*
2 A *[1 mark]*, E *[1 mark]*
3 B *[1 mark]*
4 total revenue = 15000 + 17500 + 16800 + 19300 + 21250 = £89850
average revenue = 89850 ÷ 5 = **£17 970**
[2 marks for correct answer, otherwise 1 mark for correctly calculating total revenue]
5 E.g. the firm might use temporary contracts to employ people with particular skills for a particular period of time *[1 mark]*. This means the business can employ staff members when they need them *[1 mark]*, and easily adjust the number of staff according to the needs of the business *[1 mark]*.
6 E.g. market research can be used to inform business decisions *[1 mark]*, which will reduce a business's risks *[1 mark]* and mean they're less likely to make costly mistakes *[1 mark]*.
7 Hint: there are lots of possible answers to this question. Remember, interest rates can affect businesses either directly, e.g. by affecting money they have borrowed or saved, or indirectly, e.g. by affecting consumer finances.
E.g. the business will have to pay a higher rate of interest on any money it has borrowed *[1 mark]*, which will increase its costs *[1 mark]* and leave it with less money to invest in other areas of the business *[1 mark]*.
8 How to grade your answer:
Level 0: Nothing worthy of credit. *[No marks]*
Level 1: There is some attempt to describe some consequences of training staff, but with little discussion of why these consequences benefit the business. *[1 to 2 marks]*
Level 2: A number of consequences of training staff have been described, with some discussion of why these consequences benefit the business. *[3 to 4 marks]*
Level 3: There is a detailed description of the consequences of training staff, and a clear discussion of why these consequences benefit the business. *[5 to 6 marks]*

Here are some points your answer may include:
Training staff makes them better at their jobs, which can mean they work faster.
This can make a business more productive and lower its average unit costs.
Training can help staff keep up to date with new technology.
This can give the business a competitive advantage, and may make it more productive.
Training staff is likely to motivate staff.
This can increase staff retention, which means the business won't have to recruit and train new staff so often, which will decrease its costs.

9 a) e.g. retained profits / loan / selling fixed assets / raising share capital *[1 mark]*

b) In flow production, products are made continuously on a production line *[1 mark]*. This is appropriate for Raymer's Ltd. as they are a baked-bean manufacturer so the products are likely to be identical / able to be mass produced *[1 mark]*.

c) E.g. as it's done on-the-job, the new factory workers might pick up bad habits *[1 mark]* which could lead to quality/productivity going down *[1 mark]*.

d) E.g. a supervisor will manage small teams of operational staff *[1 mark]*.

e) How to grade your answer:
Level 0: Nothing worthy of credit. *[No marks]*
Level 1: Some attempt has been made to recommend which option Raymer's Ltd. should choose, but with little justification for why this should be done. *[1 to 3 marks]*
Level 2: Some of the advantages and disadvantages of internal and external recruitment have been given, along with a recommendation of which option Raymer's Ltd. should choose. There is some reasoning to the recommendation, but it is lacking in detail or not fully justified. *[4 to 6 marks]*
Level 3: There is a detailed explanation of the advantages and disadvantages of internal and external recruitment, with a well-reasoned and fully justified recommendation of what Raymer's Ltd. should do. *[7 to 9 marks]*

Here are some points your answer may include:
Internal recruitment
Promoting and training existing staff would boost staff motivation. This is likely to make staff more productive as they will feel valued and so will want the business to do well. Therefore they will do their jobs as best they can to help that to happen. Increased productivity could lead to increased profits for the firm. More motivated staff are also more likely to stay with the firm. This could reduce Raymer's Ltd.'s recruitment and training costs in the future.
Recruiting internally would mean that Raymer's Ltd. save money on advertising the job externally.
It would also mean that the new supervisors already know a lot about the company, so they may need less training than an external recruit.
It would also mean that managers would know the candidate already, so they would have an idea of how suitable they were for the supervisor role. This may save time and money on recruiting an external candidate and then later finding out that they were not right for the job.

Recruiting internally would mean that Raymer's Ltd. have to recruit new factory workers to replace those that had been promoted to supervisor, but they would need to recruit new factory workers anyway as part of the expansion, so this is unlikely to cost too much more.
External recruitment
Another local food manufacturing company has recently gone out of business, so it's likely that there will be unemployed people in the area with supervisor experience that Raymer's Ltd could employ. These people might require less training than some of the existing factory workers.
Recruiting externally would also mean that the new staff may be able to share some of their ideas and experiences from other jobs and introduce more productive ways of working.
It's likely that recruiting externally would give the firm more candidates to choose from, so they would have more chance of finding someone that is well suited to the role.
However, recruiting externally may take more time, as well as money, than recruiting internally. This might be a problem if the firm wants to expand quickly and needs to find staff as quickly as possible.

You need to finish your answer with a conclusion recommending what you think Raymer's Ltd. should do — make sure you've looked thoroughly at all the information given. E.g. 'Raymer's Ltd. should fill the new supervisor positions by promoting existing factory workers. This will make staff feel more motivated, which may make them more productive and more likely to stay with the firm. It will also save money on recruitment and training costs.'

10 a) internal growth / organic growth *[1 mark]*

b) Stock levels are kept as low as possible *[1 mark]* by ensuring that raw materials arrive, are made into products and leave just in time for delivery to customers *[1 mark]*.

c) E.g. Diggitup Ltd. are able to use a Chinese wood supplier *[1 mark]*, which is cheaper than a UK supplier *[1 mark]*.

d) 2007 net profit margin = (net profit ÷ revenue) × 100
= (164 000 ÷ 800 000) × 100 = 20.5%
difference in profit margins = 20.5 − 18.2 = **2.3%**
[3 marks for correct answer, otherwise 1 mark for using the correct equation to calculate net profit margin, 1 mark for correct calculation of 2007 net profit margin]

e) total profit = 120000 + 190000 + 210000 + 230000 + 240000 + 235000 + 215000 + 160000 − 250000
= £1 350 000
average annual profit = 1350000 ÷ 8 = £168 750
average rate of return = (168 750 ÷ 250 000) × 100
= **67.5%**
[4 marks for correct answer, otherwise 1 mark for correctly calculating total profit, 1 mark for correctly calculating average annual profit and 1 mark for using the correct equation to calculate the average rate of return]

f) How to grade your answer:
Level 0: Nothing worthy of credit. *[No marks]*
Level 1: There is some attempt to describe the impact of selling SpadeAce in branches of Maxi Store on Diggitup Ltd., but with little explanation of the advantage and disadvantage to the firm. *[1 to 2 marks]*

Level 2: There is a good description of the impact of selling SpadeAce in branches of Maxi Store on Diggitup Ltd., with some explanation of the advantage and disadvantage to the firm. *[3 to 4 marks]*

Level 3: There is a detailed description of the impact of selling SpadeAce in branches of Maxi Store on Diggitup Ltd., and a clear explanation of the advantage and disadvantage to the firm. *[5 to 6 marks]*

Here are some points your answer may include:
Sales of gardening products at Maxi Store increased from 4% of total non-food sales in 2005 to 9% in 2007. This suggests that demand from the supermarket's customers for gardening products increased during that time. If this growth continued, then selling the SpadeAce through Maxi Store may have meant that Diggitup Ltd.'s revenue continued to grow over time as well, and as a result its profit increased.

It may have been difficult for Diggitup Ltd. to supply enough of the SpadeAce to Maxi Store on time. This is because it uses a just-in-time method of stock control which means that it would not have had stock left over from the previous period to help fulfill the order. The late deliveries of wood would also have affected the ability of Diggitup Ltd. to make and supply the SpadeAce to Maxi Store on time.

Not being able to fulfill orders with Maxi Store may have affected Diggitup Ltd's relationship with the supermarket chain. If the Maxi Store chain stopped buying from Diggitup Ltd., not only would the company have lost out on revenue, but it may have damaged its reputation with other stores and affected its ability to grow.

g) How to grade your answer:
Level 0: Nothing worthy of credit. *[No marks]*
Level 1: Some advantages and disadvantages of changing the wood supplier are given, but with little explanation of whether Diggitup Ltd. would have benefitted overall. *[1 to 4 marks]*
Level 2: There is a detailed description of the advantages and disadvantages of changing wood supplier. There is some attempt to conclude whether Diggitup Ltd. would benefit overall from changing wood supplier, but with little or no explanation to justify the conclusion. *[5 to 8 marks]*
Level 3: There is a detailed and thorough analysis of the advantages and disadvantages of changing wood supplier. A conclusion has been made as to whether Diggitup Ltd. will benefit from changing wood supplier, which has been fully justified using evidence. *[9 to 12 marks]*

Here are some points your answer may include:
Choosing the right supplier should help to ensure a firm's products are high quality, that a firm's costs are controlled, and that customers are satisfied with their product.
Diggitup Ltd. chose to change to a supplier that is more expensive than their previous supplier. This will have increased their costs, and so may have reduced their profits.

The UK supplier provides wood at a more consistent quality than the Chinese supplier. This means that Diggitup Ltd. would have reduced its waste from products that weren't the right quality, or material that they couldn't use. This will have reduced Diggitup Ltd.'s costs.

The UK supplier is more reliable at delivering the wood than the Chinese supplier, this means that Diggitup would have been better able to supply its products to shops on time than with the previous supplier. This could have helped Diggitup Ltd. to fulfil its orders to stores like Maxi Store, and to increase Diggitup Ltd.'s sales and profit.

The wood from the UK supplier is sustainably sourced. This may have meant that environmentally conscious customers are more likely to have decided to buy the SpadeAce, which would have increased Diggitup Ltd's sales.

You need to finish your answer with a conclusion about whether changing wood supplier would have been beneficial for Diggitup Ltd. — make sure you've looked thoroughly at all the information given. E.g. 'Changing to the new supplier would have been beneficial overall for Diggitup Ltd. This is because they would have saved money from using a better quality wood, been able to fulfil their orders on time to stores like Maxi Store and their sales may have increased due to the trend in people becoming more environmentally conscious.'

11 a) e.g. personal savings / share capital / venture capital / crowd funding *[1 mark]*

b) A sole trader business is owned by just one person *[1 mark]*, whereas a partnership has at least two and generally up to twenty partners who own the business *[1 mark]*.

c) E.g. reliable research will represent the information Richard and Harry are interested in more accurately *[1 mark]* meaning they will be able to make better decisions for the business *[1 mark]*.

d) Richard and Harry segmented the market by age *[1 mark]* by developing products to target two different age categories *[1 mark]*.

e) E.g. Skin Easy has products of lower quality compared to Clear Skin *[1 mark]*, so customers might not be satisfied with Skin Easy's products *[1 mark]*.

f) E.g. Clear Skin aims to pay a fair price for its raw materials *[1 mark]*, so its suppliers will benefit from an increased income *[1 mark]*.

g) total repayment = 48 × 200 = £9600
interest = (9600 − 8000) ÷ 8000 × 100 = **20%** *[3 marks for correct answer, otherwise 1 mark for correctly calculating total repayment, 1 mark for using the correct equation to calculate interest]*

h) How to grade your answer:
Level 0: Nothing worthy of credit. *[No marks]*
Level 1: Some attempt has been made to recommend which option Clear Skin should choose, but with little justification for why this is the better option. *[1 to 3 marks]*
Level 2: Some of the advantages and disadvantages to Clear Skin of each option have been given, along with a recommendation of which option Clear Skin should choose. There is some reasoning to the recommendation, but it is lacking in detail or not fully justified. *[4 to 6 marks]*

Level 3: There is a detailed explanation of the advantages and disadvantages to Clear Skin of each option, with a well-reasoned and fully justified recommendation of what Clear Skin should do. *[7 to 9 marks]*

Here are some points your answer may include:

Option 1

Setting up a social media account would have allowed Clear Skin to communicate more easily with their customers. The company would have been able to share information in many different forms, including written messages, pictures, videos or links to other sites. This would have meant that Clear Skin could easily have used the social media accounts for many different purposes, including advertising their products or providing customer service. This may have raised their profile and made people more aware of the brand, meaning they would have been more likely to buy Clear Skin's products.

Setting up a social media account would have been cheap, so it shouldn't have affected Clear Skin's costs.

Option 2

The size of Clear Skin's product range is currently a weakness of the company since it is much smaller compared to that of their competitors.

Increasing their product range may have meant that Clear Skin would have been more attractive to customers. This may have increased demand, and so increased their market share.

Developing products would have been expensive. As the business is relatively young, they might not have had enough money to invest in developing products. If the products didn't sell as well as predicted, the business could have failed.

You need to finish your answer with a conclusion recommending what you think Clear Skin should have done — make sure you've looked thoroughly at all the information given. E.g. 'Clear Skin should have set up a social media account. This way they could have quickly made more people aware of their products, and so increased their market share without a significant increase in costs.'

i) How to grade your answer:

Level 0: Nothing worthy of credit. *[No marks]*

Level 1: Some advantages and disadvantages of the changing economic climate on Clear Skin are given, but with little explanation of whether Clear Skin would have benefitted overall. *[1 to 4 marks]*

Level 2: There is a detailed description of the advantages and disadvantages that the changing economic climate would have on Clear Skin. There is some attempt to conclude whether Clear Skin would have benefitted overall, but with little or no explanation to justify the conclusion. *[5 to 8 marks]*

Level 3: There is a detailed and thorough analysis of the advantages and disadvantages that the changing economic climate may have on Clear Skin. A conclusion has been made as to whether Clear Skin would have benefitted overall, which has been fully justified using evidence. *[9 to 12 marks]*

Here are some points your answer may include:

A rise in unemployment means that more people are out of work, and so many people have less money available to spend.

The unemployment rate increased from 5.2% to 7.8% between the start of 2008 and the end of 2009. This means it's likely that consumer spending would have gone down.

Clear Skin's products are not necessities, so it is likely that demand for them may have fallen as the unemployment rate rose.

A low interest rate means that it is cheaper to borrow money, and less interest is paid on money saved in the bank. This can cause people to spend more and save less. The Bank of England base rate for interest decreased from 5.5% to 0.5% between the start of 2008 and the end of 2009. This means that most other interest rates are also likely to have fallen sharply within this time period. This means that consumer spending may have increased, which could have caused Clear Skin's sales to increase.

The falling interest rates would also have meant that Clear Skin paid less in interest repayments on their loan. This fall in business costs would have meant they had more money available to invest in the business.

The value of the British pound against the rupee fell by 2.9 between the start of 2008 and the end of 2009. This would have meant that it became more expensive for Clear Skin to import its raw materials. This would have left them with less money to invest in the business.

If the extra costs of raw materials outweighed the reduced costs of the bank loan, Clear Skin could have increased their prices to cover these extra costs. However, this may have led to a decline in sales, which would have made it more difficult for them to grow the business.

You need to finish your answer with a conclusion whether or not Clear Skin would have benefitted from the changing economic climate — make sure you've looked thoroughly at all the information given. E.g. 'Although falling interest rates may have reduced some of Clear Skin's costs, the rise in exchange rate may have increased costs. Also, rising unemployment rates are likely to have reduced consumer spending, meaning that demand for Clear Skin's products may have fallen. This fall in consumer spending is likely to have resulted in Clear Skin suffering overall from the changing economic climate.'

BUEQ41